AEROTOXIC SYNDROME

John Hoyte was born in 1955. He was a professional pilot for nearly 30 years, working in aerial crop spraying and fire fighting, as a public transport pilot of both freight and passengers, and a flying instructor. However in 1990, while flying the BAe 146 airliner he succumbed to mysterious ill health, which led him to take premature retirement on medical grounds in 2005. In 2006 he became aware of aerotoxic syndrome, and this led him on a voyage of discovery, working with scientists, doctors and other aircrew to have the illness formally recognized and known solutions implemented. He founded the Aerotoxic Association in 2007. He lives in Norwich, and has two wonderful children.

Aerotoxic Syndrome

Aviation's Darkest Secret

John Hoyte

John Hoyte
5th March 2015

First published 2014
by
Pilot Press
27 Old Gloucester Street
London WC1N 3AX
United Kingdom

British Library Cataloguing in Publication Data
A catalogue record for this book is available from the British Library

ISBN-13:
Paperback 978-0-9929508-0-4
Ebook 978-0-9929508-1-1

10 9 8 7 6 5 4 3 2 1

Designed and typeset by Curran Publishing Services, Norwich, UK
Printed by CPI Antony Rowe, Chippenham, Wilts, UK

'To this day, the only thing filtering this toxic soup out of the cabin are the lungs of the passengers and crew.'

This quote, from US aviation attorney Alisa Brodkowitz in 2010, following a legal challenge to Boeing, should give an idea of the content of this book: it concerns an inconvenient health risk known for over 60 years which can affect anyone who sets foot on board a jet aircraft.

The purpose of this book is to raise awareness of a hidden problem in aviation. As it involves the air that all of us breathe, it is applicable to aircrew and passengers alike.

The author experienced extreme ill health whilst he flew the BAe 146 airliner, but was he alone? How does the air become poisoned? Why are doctors not told about this? Why have known solutions not as yet been introduced? These and many other questions are answered in the account that follows.

Dedicated to the founders of aerotoxic syndrome

Professor Chris Winder (1952–2014)
Dr Harry Hoffman (1942–2004)
and
Dr Jean-Christophe Balouet

and to all those individuals around the world who have suffered from exposure to contaminated air on commercial aircraft

Contents

Preface and acknowledgements

I am indebted to journalist and author Philip Whiteley for his help with research for this book. As a member of the Chartered Management Institute (CMI), Philip warned me that his findings were serious. They led to the publication of a dossier (see http://aerotoxic.org/news/the-aerotoxic-dossier/) in February 2014; he felt he had a duty to report on the 'Employer's duty of care in airlines – suspected breaches'.

I originally planned to write this book for my family, as a chronological testimony of my flying career and my personal discovery of aerotoxic syndrome in 2006, but I soon realized that aerotoxic syndrome is of interest to a much wider audience, and that a book about it called for less detail about my personal life and early flying career. I invited publisher and author Susan Curran to help me combine the account of my experiences with information on the overall issue of aerotoxicity, and she has played an invaluable role in presenting the finished book.

John Williams, of the Edgbaston book club, is an avid reader and friend who spurred me into action.

Captain Peter Lawton, who taught me to fly, and shared many of my experiences as a fellow crop-spraying and airline pilot, has ensured the accuracy of flying detail.

Jonathan Perkins has done excellent work as my personal assistant, generally keeping the book on course and taking responsibility for its production. I could never have achieved it without his cheerful assistance.

I am indebted to David Learmount, safety editor of *Flight International,* for his Foreword to this book and support over the years while daring to report inconvenient news in his distinguished industry journal.

I am keen to recognize the testimonies from other aircrew, many of whom prefer to remain anonymous because they are still employed in the industry or taking legal action.

I have always known that solving a problem such as aerotoxic syndrome could not be done alone, and I am indebted to the following individuals who I have got to know over the years and who have done more than their bit to bring about known solutions: Dr Sarah Mackenzie Ross, UCL; Professor Clem Furlong, University of Washington, USA; Professor Abou-Donia, Duke University, North Carolina, USA; Dr Sarah Myhill; Dr Jean-Christophe Balouet; the late Professor Chris Winder; Professor Chris Van Netten; Rev. John Woodley; Dr Jonathan Burdon; Dr Michel Mulder; Margaret, Countess of Mar; Lord Paul Tyler; Judith Anderson (formerly Murawski), AFA-CWA, AFL-CIO; John Lind; Professor Jeremy Ramsden; Frank Taylor, Air Safety Group; Frank Cannon, Cannons Law Practice; Frank Brehany, Holiday Travel Watch; Ian Panton; Nick Cook, ROSPA; the late Richard Westgate and the Westgate family; Captain Julian Soddy; Captain Phillip 'Tango'; Bob Millichap; Len Lawrence; Deanne Wientge; Dee Passon; Captain Tony Watson (who spent three years updating the Aerotoxic Association website); Andrew Gibbs; Bee Beaumont; Ted Jeory and the *Sunday Express*; the late Paul Foot and *Private Eye*; Tim van Beveren, aviation journalist; Becky Dutton; Brenda Sutcliffe; Theresa Layton; Stephanie Trotter OBE, CO Gas Safety; Halvor Erikstein, SAFE; Christine Standing (MA); Capt. Ray Ronan, co-author of *Seconds to Disaster*; Peter Jackson, former IPA General Secretary; the late Susie Anderson; Capt. Trefor Mercer; Capt. Ray Godfrey; Capt. Tim Lindsay and First Officer Karen Lysakowska. Apologies to anyone I have forgotten.

Note that some names have been changed to protect the identities of those still working within the aviation industry.

My greatest appreciation must be reserved for Captain Tristan Loraine and Dr Susan Michaelis, both of the Global Cabin Air Quality Executive (GCAQE), fellow pilots who became ill from exposure to oil fumes and have worked tirelessly for others. They also saved my life in 2006.

My thanks are due too to those who provided the illustrations in this book. Every effort has been made to contact the rights holders, but in a few cases this has not proved possible; I should be glad to provide full credit in future editions to those whose work it has not been possible to credit fully here.

Since I began flying, I have always been convinced that difficulties, however large or small, can be overcome eventually, but only once sufficient evidence exists to bring about change.

I am certain that when public courts view the available evidence, including sworn testimonies and actual concentrations of chemicals in fume events, known solutions will be rapidly forthcoming.

This book has undergone a process of *peer review*, which for those unfamiliar with the term, is an evaluation of work done by those in the same field, most commonly the academic field. This is not an academic work, it is a layperson's introduction to the issue. Nevertheless, this book has been reviewed by over 20 experts, from aircrew to government scientists from both sides of the discourse, over a period of three months, in an effort to present the facts in the most accurate way possible.

None of the above, however, bear any responsibility for what I have written, nor can any of them necessarily be associated with my views

Copies of this book can be found in the Bodleian Library, Oxford; Cambridge University Library; National Library of Scotland; Library of Trinity College Dublin; National Library of Wales; Ottawa Public Library; Auckland City Libraries; New York Public Library; National Library of Australia (Canberra); New South Wales State Library (Sydney); and the University of New South Wales Library (Sydney).

John Hoyte
October 2014

Public notice

Please note that there is no relationship between Nicki Hoyte (Norgate) currently trading as Ladbroke Consulting & Training, Warwickshire, UK, and the author.

Accuracy means something to me. It's vital to my sense of values. I've learned not to trust people who are inaccurate. Every aviator knows that if mechanics are inaccurate, aircraft crash. If pilots are inaccurate, they get lost—sometimes killed. In my profession life itself depends on accuracy.

Charles A. Lindbergh, *The Spirit of St Louis*, 1953

The most dangerous phrase in the language is 'We've always done it this way.'

Anon.

It is difficult to get a man to understand something, when his salary depends on his not understanding it.

Upton Sinclair

Foreword

Aerotoxic syndrome exists. But so does systematic denial by the aviation industry and its government backers.

As an aviation journalist for 35 years at the time of writing this Foreword, for a long time I believed the industry when it told me, hand on heart, that the dangers to pilot and passenger health of engine oil fumes entering aircraft cabins were dramatically exaggerated and very rare. But eventually I agreed to meet two former airline pilots who had suffered damage and lost their careers to aerotoxic syndrome. I had, however, met others before and had not been convinced, so what made the difference this time?

Tristan Loraine and Susan Michaelis provided me with the technical data and evidence of something that had been going on for years – about 50 years. They informed me about the chemicals involved, the ongoing biochemical research into the damage these can cause to humans, the fume event occurrences and what makes them happen, and the human stories of pilots and cabin crew affected. And through them I met a network of aeromedical specialists and biochemists who were studying the issue in detail.

Then I started asking questions again in the industry, but I was much better informed this time.

No aircraft or aero-engine manufacturer denies that fumes from engine oil can get into cockpits and cabins, nor do they deny that these 'fume events' happen from time to time. They do not deny either that these engine oils contain organophosphate materials that can cause neurological damage in humans. The oil containers even have warnings on them to that effect.

The reason the industry and its government backers can keep the lid on this issue is that the burden of proof about the damage these fumes can cause rests with the victims. The industry answers charges about health damage by denial and dissembling, which the system lets them do because of the rules about where the burden of proof lies. The industry's lawyers are masters of technical points of law that enable them to claim that the victims have no legal proof of the connection between a fume event and the symptoms that the victims suffer as a result. The lawyers can argue that the cause might lie elsewhere in the victim's life, or in their metabolism, and this 'negative' allegation is very difficult to disprove.

There is a precise parallel here between the legal war fought for years between the tobacco industry and damaged smokers and the medical world who were looking for the proof of a connection between tobacco smoking and lung cancer. Everybody knew that there was a connection, but the burden of proof was with the victims, and until a precise biomarker could establish that the cancer was initiated by the effects of tobacco-based chemicals in specific individuals who smoked, the industry could go on denying.

The only difference between these two cases is one of scale. The health effects of tobacco affected billions of people worldwide, whereas although aircraft fume events happen regularly, they only occur once every several hundred flights. And when they do, some individuals are affected while others are not, because of metabolic differences between individual humans and the frequency of exposure that any individual suffers. The fact that fewer people are involved makes it easier for the industry and government to continue the denial, and more difficult for those damaged to seek any form of redress – or even acknowledgement of their medical condition. It means ordinary doctors are kept in ignorance of the syndrome and its symptoms, making misdiagnosis more likely.

The fact is that, for those who are affected, the effect of aerotoxic syndrome on their lives can be devastating. For that reason it is obscene that the industry washes its hands of the issue, and even worse that governments collude, because there are ways of reducing or even eliminating the risk of airborne fume events. But while denial exists and governments collude with the manufacturers and airlines, these remedies will not be applied. That is what this book is about.

David Learmount,
Operations and safety editor, *Flight International*

1

A pilot walks

On 29 August 2004 I was scheduled to fly a Flybe BAe 146 from Birmingham to Salzburg. But should I fly the aircraft? Or should I tell the airline I wasn't fit enough to fly, and leave? Sitting in the cockpit on the apron at Birmingham airport, I was sweating and uncomfortable as I tried to decide.

Not feeling too well was not new to me; I had been unwell almost continuously since I had started flying BAe 146s in 1989. But my health problems had become more threatening over the previous few months, and that day was particularly bad. I felt confused and dizzy, yet calm. My memory was impaired, and my hand–eye coordination was shot to pieces.

On the plus side, I had been flying the BAe 146 for fifteen years, and had been a pilot for a quarter of a century. Under normal circumstances, flying an aircraft came easily to me. I found it no harder than riding a bike. Even feeling as I did, I knew I could just about cope with the routines for taking off, cruising and landing in normal conditions.

But the conditions were not normal. In aviation safety training, we are taught the 'Swiss cheese' model. Imagine slices of Swiss cheese with irregular holes in them. Each slice represents an element which could contribute to an accident or incident. Now swivel them around on top of one another. For the most part, the holes don't line up, and the arrow of the accident cannot pass through. If the holes in each slice are allowed to come into alignment and you can see all the way through, the accident is free to take place. Then it is up to the pilots to prevent the final slice from lining up. This powerful risk assessment tool invented by Professor James Reason is drilled into pilots during their training.

This was one of my more serious 'Swiss cheese' moments in my quarter-century of flying: I might have to actually use the model for real.

Problem one was my condition, and my seriously impaired motor skills and cognitive abilities.

Problem two was Salzburg, our destination. Airfields are graded for the difficulty of take-off and landing, running from A (the safest) to C (the most tricky; typically an airfield in a mountainous region, with limited runway length or peculiar weather conditions). Most airfields used for commercial flights are category A, but Salzburg is not; it's a category B.

Problem three was the weather. The local weather forecast on arrival was terrible, with unpredictable thunderstorms expected.

Problem four was the state of the crew. We had all experienced multiple major roster changes and I was due to act as a first officer for a captain who had never been to Salzburg before, so I could not comfortably leave the approach and landing to him.

Problem five was the fuel onboard: we only had just enough for the flight, and could run into difficulties if we had to delay landing and then divert to another airport.

All the holes lined up: pilots, destination airport, weather, crew, fuel. The point of safety training is that it is supposed to keep you safe; ask a safety expert what I should do in that situation, and they would surely have told me to not fly. Ask the passengers, and they would probably have told me the same: that their desire to reach Salzburg was not nearly as strong as their unwillingness to end up being strewn across an Austrian alp. You might well think it a shocking indictment of the state of the aviation industry today that I should ever have thought of this as a dilemma.

But it certainly seemed to me that I did. In many jobs, people who feel as unwell as I felt at that moment would automatically cry off sick, but that's not the ethos among commercial pilots. There is much psychological pressure placed on aircrew to fulfil their assignments unless they absolutely cannot do so, and if they do opt to pull out, they cannot expect much sympathy from their bosses. However strong the arguments against flying seemed to me, I believed I would land in big trouble if I gave in to them.

Even so, I decided I'd have to face that trouble, and get out of the cockpit. I told my colleague on the flight deck how I felt and walked off the aircraft, out of Birmingham airport and I drove home.

Did I get into trouble as a result? More trouble than I had ever imagined up to that moment. The decision I made that day was to lead to a seemingly endless series of battles with the airline, aviation regulators, the wider industry, its doctors, advisers and the government. Those battles have not ended yet. But just as I knew I shouldn't fly that day, I also know I had to keep going with the subsequent battles. The ill-health symptoms I was experiencing were not unique, they are common to many aircrew, and to passengers as well. Not all sick aircrew make the choice I made, and I do not blame them for that, because they face a terrible outcome whichever choice they make. That this is the case should worry anyone who ever gets into a jet aircraft.

The fact that I was too ill to fly that day wasn't bad luck. It wasn't my imagination. It wasn't my fault either. If it was anyone's, it was the airline industry's.

2

Flying makes people ill

Workers in the airline industry have a very high sickness rate. For example, the US Department of Labor found that scheduled passenger air transportation (private industry) had a level of sickness and injury calling for days off work in 2011 and 2012 that was more than three times higher than the average rate for all industries, local and state government workers.[1] Other studies across the world have repeatedly found much the same situation: I summarize some of them in the next chapter.

A lot of factors contribute to a rate like this, of course. It's not that the rate of air accidents causing physical injury is significant: that accounts for only a minuscule proportion of those lost days. Commentators often point to issues such as the unsocial nature of aircrews' work. It's a job that doesn't lend itself to regular hours and a straightforward family and social life. But if this predisposes aircrew to take the odd 'sickie' when they maybe really don't need to, a lot of factors dispose them in the other direction.

I was a typical airline pilot in many ways. As a profession, pilots tend to be younger than the average across the workforce. They need a good level of intelligence, and an even higher level of persistence and commitment, to gain the qualifications that are called for. They love flying; this is not a job that people do just for the money. They tend to be fit, sporty types – at least, before they start work on airlines. The job is not available to those who already have serious health problems. Aircrew have stable temperaments, and are good in a crisis. They are not complainers – they tend to downplay their own problems and get on with whatever needs doing. And they are well aware that this is a profession where taking time off – particularly at short notice – causes a lot of inconvenience to others. On balance, does this mean that aircrew are particularly disposed to overplay their ailments and take time off when they don't really need to? It doesn't look that way to me.

Perhaps the industry should be asking, then, why it is that flying commercial airliners makes some of these previously fit individuals so ill. Is it asking that? As you'll learn in this book, the broad answer is no. And when individuals such as me point them to possible answers, is it open to exploring them, and taking action? Again, the answer is one you are not going to like.

But we need to ensure that airlines, regulators and governments do listen, and do take action as a result, because the alternative is so terrible. The alternative is pilots like me, who continue flying even when they know they are not fit to do so, because they are afraid of the consequences of admitting to their problems. The alternative is passengers flying on aircraft with problems that have not been explored and dealt with; those passengers entrusting their lives to crew members who are not operating at anywhere near peak capacity; and passengers suffering from the same kinds of symptoms themselves. The alternative is aircrew who retire through ill health facing resistance and obstruction when they try to gain compensation for problems that were brought about directly by the conditions in which they worked. We should not allow any of this to continue. And we do not need to allow it to continue, because there is plenty of clear evidence of what is causing the problem, and how it can be remedied.

Before we look at this evidence, though, let me present you with some stories from other airline staff. These are all based on individual cases that are known to me at first hand, although in some cases I have changed names, because those still working in the industry are worried about the consequences if they reveal this kind of information.

A long-haul airline pilot

Don (a pseudonym) is a commercial pilot who has had a lot of experience on ultra-long range flights. For example, the Dubai to Sydney run which he covered is a 15-hour nonstop flight, while flights on his other routes last 16.5 or even 17 hours. His airline only allowed pilots to do up to four of these ultra long-range flights each month, but Don still found that he got extremely tired, particularly when he started flying an Airbus

A340-600 (a 'heavy' aircraft). His tiredness wasn't unique, many of his team were equally tired, and he put it down at first to the nature of the work and the stress of these long flights.

The 340 is notorious for its 'fume events'. Fumes from its engines seeping into the body of the aircraft cause a problem frequently enough that there is guidance in the quick-reference handbook on how to operate the aircraft in this condition. The drill calls for the engine bleed supply valve on the known 'oily bleed' engine to be switched off prior to engine start and for the flight to depart using only three of the four bleed supplies available.

Don and his team experienced a fume incident when he was captaining a flight to Melbourne. The cockpit filled with light grey smoke just after take-off. It was bad enough that the cabin manager warned him the passengers were getting very scared, and of course his job was to reassure them and to go through the prescribed drill.

In Don's words, this flight 'knocked me over'. What had been understandable weariness developed into an extreme fatigue. It reached the point where he couldn't even watch a movie in his time off without falling asleep.

He noticed other symptoms too, including problems with concentration and coordination. His driving was going downhill, and by 2012 he was aware that his flying skills were suffering too. A very experienced pilot tends to carry out his duties almost by instinct, but instead of the routine growing easier with familiarity, Don found it becoming harder. His hand–eye coordination had become much worse. His short-term memory suffered too, to the extent that he couldn't remember vital air traffic control instructions such as whether his flight had been cleared to land.

Don completed a short regional flight on the A340 with no noticeable smells or smoke. It involved an early start, and when he felt terrible afterwards, initially he blamed that. Three days later he came down with what he took to be a cold or very bad chest infection. He went to the company doctor, but the prescription he was given didn't help.

A few days after this flight he was asked to attend a disciplinary/HR meeting, which was concerned with the increasing amount of sickness absence he had been taking.

Don was feeling bad enough that he subsequently told the

company doctor he was worried that his overall flying skills were deteriorating. No pilot likes to admit such a thing, and Don wouldn't have done so had his concern not been so serious. The company doctor seemed to think that his problem might be related to extreme overwork, that the long flights had effectively burned him out, and that they should look at a computer evaluation of his previous six months' roster. This made sense to Don, but when he was called back to see the doctor a few days later the attitude had changed. He was sent for sleep analysis, which didn't make much sense to him, because he hadn't reported having any sleep problems.

It became obvious at this point that the company doctor had been 'compromised' and had been instructed to find something else wrong with Don.

Don consulted a private doctor, and was advised to try a homeopathic remedy. That didn't work either. And he continued to see the company doctors, whose diagnoses still centred on sleep disorders. But at the same time he talked to a pilot he had learned to fly with twenty years earlier. This man flew BAe 146s, another plane notorious for its smoke problems, and he was suffering from symptoms very much like Don's. He was in contact with a network of aviation people who were concerned that the cause of these symptoms was not sleep disorders, but poisoning from the substances in the fumes. But Don's company doctors didn't support any idea other than sleep disorders; they kept on treating him as if his problem was a sleeping difficulty. He even went for a second 'sleep analysis', which showed no sign of any problem.

By this time, Don was anxious to get back to work. His company's sick pay deal wasn't great: he got a month's full pay, then two months on half pay, then that was it. He had a mortgage to pay. He returned as an instructor on flight simulators as his medical certificate was suspended. The company put him on a roster that was harder than his old ones had been: six days on, one day off, then five days on, one off, then six days on, and so on. He couldn't handle this, and had to take more time off sick.

Perhaps ironically, it was a flight that he took as a passenger on his own company's A340 that broke him. It made him seriously ill, with all the same symptoms he had shown from the start – coordination problems, memory problems – intensified.

This persuaded him to look more seriously at the possibility of chemical poisoning, through the network his old colleague had mentioned.

The new specialists Don contacted gave him a battery of physical tests: a brain scan, blood tests and a DNA profile test. Their assumption was that these might reveal a physical basis to what the airline had continued to see as a sleep problem. The specialists also asked him to do a 'shirt test'. He had to buy a new white shirt and then wear it on a long flight he took (as a passenger), and send it for a lab analysis. It took a few months for him to get the analysis result (which in my experience is typical for these specialized tests): the shirt had tested positive for tricresyl phosphate (TCP). This is an organophosphate chemical that is used as an additive in oil and hydraulic fluids, and which is extremely toxic to humans.

Tests of Don's hand–eye coordination and measurement of his gait flagged up serious physical problems. He also had a seriously degraded visual processing capability. Another test result showed he had a type of liver that doesn't process organophosphates efficiently, so when he absorbs these substances, they accumulate in his body and slowly poison him. An estimated 40 per cent of the population fall into this category, while for 3 per cent the liver disfunction could even more easily lead to a fatal outcome.

This means that as the individual continues to be exposed to toxins, the impact becomes worse and worse: and that was certainly Don's experience. He had reached a point when he couldn't even handle a short flight as a passenger. At the same time, many of the doctors he saw continued to insist that he was suffering from burnout, and that the only treatment he needed was rest.

Don's employers, meanwhile, demanded that he take a flight back to his base airport, and continue his work. He felt he could not possibly agree to this, and although he had still to have confirmation when my colleagues talked to him, he understands that he has now been dismissed. Although in theory he has income protection insurance, he has not yet managed to obtain any payout, not least because the company's doctors have not accepted the diagnosis of organophosphate poisoning. Don's GP knew exactly what is wrong with him but had not realized that aerotoxic syndrome falls under the UK list of 'prescribed diseases'.[2] This is fairly similar to having asbestosis in the 1960s.

What angers Don particularly is that the company are refusing to accept what seems to him very clear evidence of the cause of his problems. He's angry too because he knows there is at least a partial remedy. Filter systems that can prevent organophosphate compounds and oil degradation products from entering the aircraft environment are readily available. The problem is that airlines do not use them.

Don is even more angry that he has been left 'high and dry' with no financial income to allow him to make his best attempts at recovery. Since the NHS (the National Health Service, the UK's state health body) do not recognize his problem he is left with only private medicine to diagnose and assist recovery. He has a company 'income protection' insurance policy to compensate for loss of income, but he is not receiving any payout from it because he has been fired for refusing to return to the country where his company has its HQ. This has happened even though the company has Don's medical report stating very plainly that 'It would be extremely inadvisable [for him] to fly'.

A North American pilot

Jim (another pseudonym) is still the employee of an airline, and concerned that this account should not give any information that will identify him or the airline he works for, so I shall not name the aircraft he has flown here.

Jim started work for this company in 1979, and flew for eight and a half years as second officer on two aircraft designed prior to 1975 which were notorious for their 'dirty socks' smell. That is a description of the smell that sometimes pervades the aircraft interior, and as flight engineer, Jim's task was to record each incidence of it in the maintenance log. Jim logged these events quite frequently, and there was always the same response: the maintenance team said they had replaced the coalescer bags.

Next he spent eight years as a pilot on another plane which stank so much that the crew had nicknames for it. His wife used to ask him to shower straightaway when he got home from work, because she couldn't stand the stinky-sock smell. It came from the engines, that was clear.

In 1988 Jim started noticing that he was getting really tired. At first he put it down to hard work and lots of travel, but by the end of 1990 it had become such a problem that he couldn't do his job any more. He saw doctors about it, of course. The company doctors seemed to think this was a psychosomatic problem: that it did not have a physical cause, but was all in his mind.

This made no sense to Jim. He thought the psychosomatic diagnosis was 'garbage, frankly'. He had always been a competitive type, and when younger had performed at a high level as an amateur sportsman. As it had got to the point where he couldn't even walk up the stairs, the cause had to be real, not imagined.

From 1990 to 1992 Jim stayed at home. He was in a semi-coma; in such a bad way that he slept 18 hours a day, every single day. And he was still tired when he woke up. The doctors he consulted still couldn't suggest a cause, let alone a treatment for him. He continued to try to work out, being a man to whom fitness is important, but this made him feel 'like I was being poisoned – it was like a really bad hangover. My head would hurt; I had a pain down my spine.'

Eventually the symptoms eased, and by early 1993 he was able to go back to work once again, flying the notoriously smelly aircraft. Six months later, he woke up and was violently ill. The next day all his old symptoms had returned, and he found himself back home on sick leave for another year. He did everything he could think of to get himself better. He moved his family so he wouldn't have to commute so far. He also tried a therapy that involved soaking himself in cold water every day. It took him two hours to warm up when he got out of the cold bath, but he 'got used to it', and since it seemed to help, carried on with it for four years. He still can't really explain why it helped, but as he puts it, 'I have theories to do with brain chemistry.'

By 1998 Jim was back at work, flying not Old Stinky but a newer model of aircraft. This one too, though, had fume events from time to time. Jim was aware that this involved oil products seeping into the aircraft, but the maintenance staff didn't seem to regard it as a serious problem. They put it down to the high-efficacy particulate air (HEPA) filters or the coalescer bags; there was nothing said to suggest it might affect people's health.

Although he experienced these occasional fume events, Jim was able to work for a good decade. But at the end of 2010 he did a series of flights which almost all involved a fume event lasting 30 to 40 minutes. This happened twice on each flight, one event on climb and one on descent. 'The last one was so bad,' he says, 'the odour so offensive, we were laughing about it. I said: I'm putting my oxygen mask on.' In time the fumes dissipated.

It was after the third or fourth of these really bad fume events, in December 2010, that Jim was exercising when suddenly his right ear seemed to 'pop'. He discovered he had lost half of his hearing. A week or ten days later he went numb on his right side. He thought at first he had had a stroke, but his doctor ruled that out straight away. Two or three weeks later, the sensation changed from numbness to hypersensitivity. Just touching his face would create a sensation 'like electric guitar feedback'. This made it particularly hard to sleep. After a year or so the sensation changed and he felt a rhythmic beat, as if his heart was echoing through his ear.

Jim, the man who had stuck with the cold baths for so long, now set himself to studying neuromolecular biochemistry. The specialists he had seen thought his problem was neurological, and as Jim puts it, 'I hypothesized demyelination. I was thinking: if the face is picking up my heart beat, then the nerves are fried.' When he met other pilots with the same or similar symptoms, he cornered the company aero medical doctor who eventually told him about organophosphate poisoning – off the record for fear of corporate reprisals.

This self-made expert devised his own treatment: 'Utilizing a dietary protocol for epilepsy, ALS [amyotrophic lateral sclerosis], MS [multiple sclerosis] and Parkinson's, and cancer, recommended by Johns Hopkins Hospital and Dominic D'Agostino, PhD, Assistant Professor, College of Medicine Molecular Pharmacology and Physiology of the University of Southern Florida, the ketogenic diet (high fat) is believed to have remyelinated damaged sections of my peripheral nervous system and potentially cleansed and revitalized my mitochondria. The fat used was high doses of clean cholesterol, something known as medium chain triglycerides extracted from coconut oil. By 10 January [2011], a month later, all the nerves had stopped their unusual sensations. The sound in my ear disappeared.'

At the same time, he kept the airline involved, and worked with his union as well. The union has been supportive, but the airline less so. As Jim puts it, 'It just seems we are expendable – I've been offline almost three years. They just couldn't care less.' It's not the airline that has helped Jim discover what has caused his symptoms, and work on finding a way to ease them. He has had to do all that himself.

A retired pilot, now a health and safety academic

Susan Michaelis started flying in 1986 along Australia's east coast, but her problems did not begin until she switched to a BAe 146 in 1994. Within two months she had reoccurring throat problems. 'Whenever I turned the air on, my head would tighten up, and my throat would become husky. It got progressively worse. I had a feeling of irritation throughout my nose and throat. I had headaches, nausea and fatigue, but the throat was the really bad bit.'

Susan found her symptoms improved when she was not breathing aircraft cabin air. And she was sure what had caused it: chemicals in the engine oil. She says:

> I would smell it; I got symptoms. For two and a half years to July 1997. I was always talking to people about it, and other pilots/cabin crew at some time also complained. I would sometimes see a light haziness and misting, but mostly just a smell that would come and go at certain stages, throughout the flight.
> ... the engineers just said, 'Don't worry, it's just the oil seals failing – management knows about it.' They changed the APU [auxiliary power unit] type to try to get rid of the problem, but it didn't make any difference. I was told there was no problem breathing the oil fumes.

Susan continued at work, but it was clear to her that there was a problem. Through 1996–97 she had similar symptoms, but they increased in intensity and frequency, and they didn't recede immediately after she left the plane. It could take her around three hours to feel better. She was also becoming chemically sensitive, although she didn't know this label at the time, just that if someone was wearing perfume around her, she wanted to vomit. As well as being hypersensitive to smells, she felt lethargic and had difficulty concentrating. She also suffered from a feeling of not getting enough oxygen.

Then in July 1997 her short-term symptoms suddenly got worse. She thought she must be having a stroke, but a medical investigation one day after the flight ruled that out.

Slowly, Susan got to know of other aircrew with similar problems, although those of her colleagues who did not suffer the same way were very dismissive. Even so, some of them had a name for it. They called it 'the 146 problem'.

One of Susan's main concerns at this point was to negotiate her way out of work, given her long-term health problems. As she puts it, 'I had to go very quietly, because if I mentioned that health problems were related to oil, I wouldn't get my income payment.' (There's an established system in the airline industry where pilots who lose their licence receive a compensatory payment, and this was what Susan was depending on.) She learned that it was safe to admit to chronic fatigue and to describe the environment in which the symptoms occurred, but not to mention chemical issues, even though some of the specialist doctors she saw gave her diagnoses including 'multiple chemical sensitivity', one test showed that she had oil in her alveoli (the small cavities in the lungs), and results of a brain scan and neurological tests were found to be consistent with the effects of organophosphate poisoning.

What Susan learned from the experiences of others convinced her how seriously the airlines took this issue of diagnosis:

> It was like putting a jigsaw puzzle together. There were others in Australia who had made the connection with the oil, and CASA (the Australian Civil Aviation Safety Authority) would look to see that they wouldn't fail their medical and they wouldn't get their payment, suggesting the problem was a psychological one, rather than psychosomatic. If you made that link with the oil you were chopped off.

So she played along with this, and in late 1999, with her

employer paying out for the loss of her licence, she spoke publicly at a government inquiry. Her job was terminated shortly afterwards, in February 2000.

Susan has continued ever since to research the issues around her condition, gaining a PhD on the subject eleven years after having to medically retire as a pilot – although as she puts it:

> I don't call myself an activist or campaigner. I'm an occupational health and safety researcher. I really take offence to the words 'activist' or 'campaigner', because the industry doesn't say that they are campaigning.

What she wants to achieve is a safe workplace for aviation employees. Does it really need a campaign to get that?

3

Depression, fatigue – and cancer

Here's some more evidence of the alarmingly high level of sickness among aircrew.

The International Crew Health Survey

The following study is not by a professional scientist, but I include it because the results are so alarming. It falls into the category of initial reports indicating that more research is needed – but the most telling observation about the aviation industry concern its marked resistance to volunteering for, supporting or undertaking such research, and its tendency to downplay the significance of the findings when research is undertaken.

Former stewardess Dee Passon (whose story is told in Chapter 11) carried out a survey on toxicfreeairlines.com, a joint venture between her and affected passenger Samantha Sabatino (see Chapter 36). Together they launched the International Crew Health Survey, a privately funded research project, whose purpose is to identify the numbers of crew who suffer from occupational health problems in their working environment.[1] Results were published in the *Journal of Biological Physics and Chemistry*, based on information collected from 1,020 crew.[2] (They comprised fifty pilots and 970 cabin crew, mostly from a single major UK airline. Since these are the individuals who chose to respond, they are not necessarily representative of all airline staff.) The respondents were 44 per cent male and 56 per cent female, with an average age of 41. Only twelve claimed to have had no time off sick and no symptoms of ill health. Of the 1,008 who had noticed symptoms, 234 (23 per cent) had not taken time off sick (they had been ill while not at work, or had gone in to work in spite of their symptoms because they were worried about the consequences of taking time off). Twenty-five per cent (262 staff) had suffered bouts of long-term sickness lasting more than three weeks. The top twelve disorders with which they had been medically diagnosed were depression, irritable bowel syndrome or Crohn's disease, high blood pressure, high cholesterol, eczema/psoriasis, insomnia, migraines, pneumonia/bronchitis, asthma, chronic fatigue, miscarriage, thyroid disorders and cancer.[3]

Dee has continued the survey work, and by the time of writing had received close to 2,000 submissions.[4]

Willing to work?

In January 2014, Dee was sent a copy of an internal email from Amy James, British Airways' Head of Worldwide Cabin Crew. Addressed to all cabin crew, a section of it read:

> Over the Christmas period, we have experienced considerably high levels of absence on Worldwide. Over 500 crew colleagues are currently absent, and to put this in context, last year the number was around 370. This has had the potential to have a huge impact on our customers were it not for the outstanding efforts of our scheduling teams and the flexibility of many of our crew to cover gaps. The impact on crew colleagues is that we have had to undertake a number of mitigating actions including – moving flights to Mixed Fleet, recalling secondees, cancelling courses and denying ad hoc leave to those who requested it. I am sure you can understand that it is disappointing for those who have been affected. In the new year, I will be undertaking a full review of the absence which has occurred over this period and I will be in touch to let you know the outcome and follow up actions. In the meantime, I appreciate very much those of you who have worked hard over the last few weeks to serve our customers and to get them to their destinations for Christmas. I want to ask for your full support in running our worldwide schedule throughout the rest of the holiday period. There is an opportunity for you to help by registering interest in 'Willing to Work'. I'm also asking for your understanding and flexibility as there is likely to be further roster

> disruption to come, this is regrettable but necessary so that we do not further inconvenience our customers. Thank you.

It's worth noting the insistence that absence must be the individual's fault. There seems here to be a policy based on the assumption that 'willingness' is sufficient to ensure good health. That this is the case, and that the high level of absence was not properly investigated, seems to me (and to colleagues like Dee) to be a breach of an employer's duty of care.

A dangerous occupation

A study of US occupational health statistics ranked the most unhealthy jobs in the United States, based on analysis of data from the Occupational Information Network (O*NET), a US Department of Labor database full of detailed information on occupations. Researchers took O*NET measures of six health risks in each of the 974 occupations in the database: exposure to contaminants; exposure to disease and infection; exposure to hazardous conditions; exposure to radiation; risk of minor burns, cuts, bites, and stings; and time spent sitting, since studies show that frequent inactivity shortens your lifespan. They scored the factors on a scale from 0 to 100, with a higher score indicating an increased health risk.

Flight attendants came in as the third most risky occupation, well ahead of derrick operators in the oil and gas industry, in eleventh place. Airline pilots were one place below, at twelfth. For flight attendants, their exposure to contaminants was rated 88 on a scale of 100.[5]

4

A syndrome

The stories I told in Chapter 2 are just three of the hundreds of accounts that the association I set up, the Aerotoxic Association, has heard of over the years. My own story is a fourth. I'll mention other people's experiences throughout the book. But from these three alone, it's clear that there are common factors:

- All these are relatively young people who were well above average in health and fitness before they began work as aircrew.
- They all experienced 'fume events' or 'smoke incidents' in the aircraft they were flying, and they all discovered that some models of aircraft were particularly prone to these incidents. Many of these occurrences were bad enough to produce a strong smell, and in some cases visible fumes as well.
- All of them became sick after experiencing these incidents, and all had a similar range of symptoms: extreme fatigue, problems with hand–eye coordination and concentration, and other neurological problems. None of these were problems they had experienced previously; on the contrary, they had all regarded themselves as well above average in energy, coordination and concentration skills.
- Repeated exposure to fume incidents seemed to make these problems worse. An end to exposure (if they took time off sick, or moved to a different type of aircraft) relieved their symptoms, but only slowly. In extreme cases it would take years to recover, and some people never recovered at all.
- Further exposure after recovery brought the symptoms back, often with greater severity.
- All of them discovered a great reluctance on the part of their employers to accept any link between their health problems and the 'fume events', and a tendency for doctors also not to give serious thought to the possibility of a link.

I am not suggesting that all airline employees with health problems fall into this category. That isn't the case. Aircrew suffer from a range of health problems, just like the rest of the working population. Nor am I suggesting that all those who fly in aircraft come down with these symptoms if they experience a 'fume event'. That isn't the case either. (Don's DNA profile test suggested an explanation for that, in that some individuals' genetics make them susceptible to varying degrees of sickness. We'll take a closer look at that later in the book.)

I'm not even suggesting that all airline staff who get very tired are examples of this problem. Modern airline work *is* tiring, for both pilots and cabin crew. On many airlines the shift patterns are demanding, the turnarounds short and the flight times long. Many staff find this exhausting; it would be a wonder if they did not. But we're not dealing here with being tired at the end of a long day's work and feeling better after a good night's sleep. We're dealing with something so different that it's perhaps not helpful to use the word 'fatigue' to describe the whole thing. We're talking about the combination of extreme fatigue with other symptoms such as the coordination and concentration difficulties I, and many others, have suffered. In my experience, these problems occur together sufficiently frequently that we can give a name to them.

An Aerotox e-group started in 1998, and brought together twenty-five members worldwide. They included pilots, cabin crew, aerospace engineers and medical doctors (including one flight surgeon) as well as environmental scientists and a toxicologist. The illness itself was first given an identity as **aerotoxic syndrome** by Dr Harry Hoffman (deceased, USA), Professor Chris Winder (deceased, Australia) and Dr Jean-Christophe Balouet (France) in 1999. It was described in 2000 in a paper entitled 'Aerotoxic syndrome: adverse health effects following exposure to jet oil mist during commercial flights' by Professor Winder and Dr Balouet.[1] Dr Russ Rayman, who had been executive director of the US Aerospace Medical Association for eighteen years, invited them to give this paper to an International Congress on Occupational Health. I feel the use of 'commercial' in the title was unfortunate, as it antagonized the industry.

Despite the weight of evidence, there are people in the aviation industry who claim that 'aerotoxic syndrome' does not exist. Aerotoxic syndrome is acknowledged by the International Classification of Diseases Committee under ICD-9-CM Diagnosis Code 987.9, 'Toxic effect of unspecified gas, fume, or vapor'.[2] This covers 'toxic effect of other specified gases, fumes, or vapors; Intentional ether overdose; Mustard gas poisoning; Oxygen toxicity'; and significantly, 'Poisoning by exhaust gas in aircraft'. Aviation research scientists, aviation doctors, and those who are poisoned by such gases in aircraft cabins call the ensuing illness 'aerotoxic syndrome'.[3]

When a combination of distinctive symptoms like this occurs frequently in an occupational group such as aircrew, you might think it would ring alarm bells for employees and health and safety authorities; that doctors would consider straight off whether this is a category into which sick employees fit, and that there would be lots of dedicated research to discover what exactly is causing the problem, and how it might be cured or alleviated.

If that was the case, I wouldn't have needed to write this book.

5

The aircraft air

I have indicated that the experience of '(oil) fume events', 'contaminated air events' or 'smoke incidents' is something that sufferers of aerotoxic syndrome have in common. Now let's take a look at what these incidents consist of, and why they happen.

As anyone who has travelled on a commercial airliner knows, aircraft hold many people in a closed compartment. One important issue in designing such aircraft is to ensure that everyone has good quality air to breathe. As we all know, people breathe in oxygen (which is just one chemical component of our atmosphere, but the one that matters most to humans) and breathe out carbon dioxide. In a confined space it's necessary to find a way to ensure that the oxygen ratio remains high enough, and the carbon dioxide ratio low enough, that the atmosphere in that space is healthy for humans. The obvious way to do this is to create an air circulation system, so that the carbon dioxide-rich air is pushed out of the space, and new oxygen-rich air is brought into it.

A further complication in an aircraft (as opposed to confined spaces on land) is that commercial airliners fly at altitudes where the air is too thin to sustain human life. To make it breathable, it has to be pressurized: squashed up, as it were, so that enough molecules of oxygen (as well as nitrogen, and the other trace elements that make up the Earth's atmosphere) are available in the space to make it breathable for humans.

Over the decades since manned flight began, designers have found various ways to achieve this. The earliest jet airliners, such as the Vickers VC10, McDonnell Douglas DC8 and Boeing 707, designed in the 1950s, used fresh air which was compressed by mechanical air pumps. But since 1962, the standard system has involved cabin air being 'bled' off the jet engine. (Hence that phrase 'engine bleed' which I used on page 6.)

Jet engines compress air as part of their operating cycle.

A McDonnell Douglas DC8. Note the outside air inlets in the nose.
Source: http://upload.wikimedia.org/wikipedia/commons/7/75/Air_Transport_Int._DC8-71F_%284547915758%29.jpg (with thanks to RAF-YYC).

Before this compressed air is fed into the engine's combustion chamber, a small proportion of it is piped to the interior of the aircraft. This 'bleed air' is at high pressure and high temperature, so it is passed through heat exchangers to cool it down. It is then fed into a mixing chamber where it is combined with air that has been recirculated from the aircraft cabin. Finally, there are regulating valves that the aircrew use to feed the mixture into the cabin and the cockpit. Perhaps you will recall from the description of the fume-event routine on the Airbus A340-600 that Don flew that there are separate valves for the air outlet from each engine, so the 'engine bleeds' can be checked one by one.

Although this is a mechanically efficient system, it is one

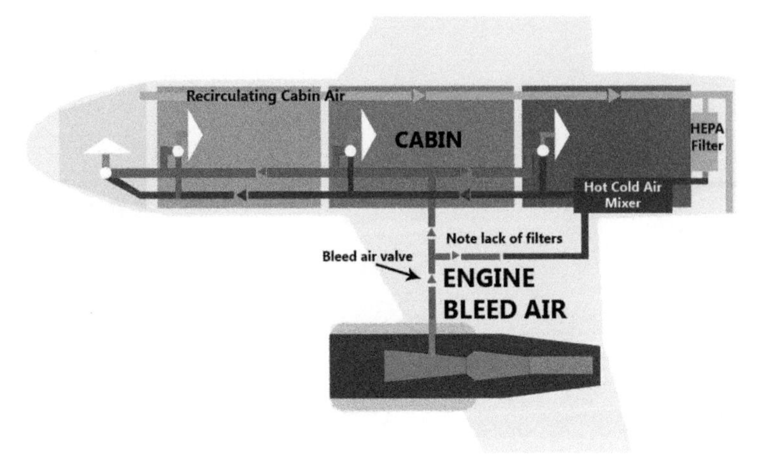

The bleed air system

with an obvious design flaw: the air has passed through part of the engine, so it inevitably comes into close proximity with the vaporized components of oil in the engine. Some of these components, as we shall see, are known to be hazardous to human health. Of course this is an issue that designers fully appreciate, just as they appreciate the dangers of repeatedly recirculating the cabin air as the other component of the mixing system. Designers use seals to keep the 'wet' (or oily) part of the engine separate from the air that is bled to the cabin, and use HEPA (high efficiency particulate air) filters, mentioned in Jim's story, to remove viruses, bacteria, dust and fibres. HEPA filters only filter the recirculated cabin air. They are not used for the bleed air, because they cannot withstand the temperature at which it enters the system.

Carbon filters are not currently fitted to passenger airliners but could be used here; they are insensitive to extreme temperatures, but at normal temperatures they are good at eliminating toxins and unpleasant smells, albeit at the price of lowering the mechanical efficiency of the system, since the air has to be forced through the filters. Indeed, a European engineering firm *has* fitted carbon filters to the fleet of an international freight company (although neither company can be named here for legal reasons) for the benefit of the pilots in the cockpit only – not the cabin.

The coalescer bags that Jim was told had been replaced are

A Boeing 787 Dreamliner. Note the outside air inlets on the fuselage at the wing-roots.
Source: http://vimeo.com/36084650. Photo: Changkyu Kim.

another part of the air conditioning system, used to collect water mist from the air.

So the essential truth remains: the bleed air supply is unfiltered. That is obvious from the very fact that 'fume events' and 'smoke incidents' are relatively common. (It has been estimated that there were an average of 0.86 fume events *every day* in the United States in 2008. We revisit this in Chapter 26.[1]) This is true particularly in some models of aircraft, and some individual 'rogue' airframes.

It is no secret what the fumes that appear in the cabin consist of: they are oil fumes from the engines that have not been kept out by the seals. These fumes tend to appear particularly when the system is started up, or during power changes, although sometimes there are fumes throughout a flight.

Designers work continually to improve the air circulation system, and it is predicted that the era of bleed air is coming to an end. One important new aircraft, the Boeing 787 Dreamliner, uses a system that does not involve bleed air, and if the dangers of bleed air were more fully appreciated, perhaps the phase-out and replacement of this technology would come all the sooner. Meanwhile, here's a good tip for both aircrew and passengers: if you have to fly, make sure you fly on a B 787 Dreamliner!

Here's a story from my own experience that shows what impact this has in real life.

A visible fume event on board a US Airways flight #432 from Phoenix, Arizona to Maui, Hawaii on 17 September 2010
Taken by an unknown amateur photographer.

I had a long spell as a BAe 146 pilot from 1989 to 2005. An important part of getting any aircraft ready to embark passengers is to bring the cabin up to temperature, and for this, power is needed. Power on the ground is supplied by an auxiliary power unit (APU). This is a small jet engine at the rear of the aircraft which provides both electrical power and bleed air. For the first flight of the day, we would start the APU, complete our pre-flight checks, and meanwhile give the cabin time to reach a comfortable temperature. During this process the cabin and cockpit would frequently fill up with visible dense white oil smoke.

This experience was by no means unique to our BAe 146s; it was common across the world. Here's Chuck Ross, an American BAe 146 pilot, commenting on the procedure in a 2008 magazine article:

> Pneumatics worked fine, it was the air conditioning system that gave rookie first officers nightmares. The Brits told us when we power the airplane up in the morning, just take the cockpit and cabin temperature controllers and 'set them

> to twelve-o-clock and forget about them'. Well, if you did that you would fill the cabin with acrid smoke that not only burned your eyes, but smelled downright carcinogenic. Passengers would take one whiff and refuse to board. Weepy, red-eyed sniffling flight attendants could not persuade them all was well.[2]

This was a 'fume event', of course, and one that happened frequently when the aircraft was powered up. These fume events never, ever got reported as a safety incident. Ask any BAe 146 pilot and they will tell you this is an unavoidable consequence of the start-up routine, so we learned to take it in our stride. Of course everyone on the crew, in both the cabin and the cockpit, was aware that breathing fumes in a confined space cannot be good for your health, so the cabin crew did their best to dissipate the visible smoke. They opened the doors to try to waft it out, because we didn't want the passengers to experience what Chuck described above. But even if this meant the passengers escaped the worst of it, the crew were all exposed to the fumes for around ten minutes at the start of every flying day.

Burning eyes is not pleasant, but it's a minor inconvenience. It wasn't until I started to experience much more serious and persistent symptoms that I really started to think back about what these fume incidents had meant for me. Then I did some basic calculations. I had been flying 146s for sixteen years, and had started the APU from cold around three times a week. If on average I had breathed in ten minutes of fumes at each start-up, then I had been exposed to these fumes for a total of around 400 hours. That's about sixteen days and nights worth of breathing in fume-filled spaces. (This isn't counting the other fume events I experienced during flights, and there were a few of those too, some of them serious.)

When those symptoms caught up with me, did anyone suggest that toxic fumes might have played a part? Far from it; the standard reaction was that it was all in my mind.

You might think, too, that if this was such a standard experience, it would be one that airlines and safety authorities would be looking at very seriously. We'll learn just how seriously they took it throughout the rest of this book.

6

Organophosphate poisoning: a long history

Every time a government requests more research on issues such as organophosphate (OP) poisoning and aerotoxic syndrome, it typically ignores what has already been reported by previous research. Most famously, the problems were spelled out in the United Kingdom way back in 1951, when Professor Solly Zuckerman chaired a working party which produced a report for the Agriculture Minister called 'Toxic Chemicals in Agriculture'. While discussing OP chemicals, Professor Zuckerman repeatedly warned that the main danger was from chronic effects. He wrote about how chronic effects could arise:

> Successive small doses of parathion [an OP] may progressively lower the cholinesterase level without producing symptoms, but may render the individual increasingly susceptible to further doses.[1]

Airlines seem to dispute just about every aspect of the aerotoxic issue, but one thing they cannot seriously dispute is where the substances come from that create the 'fume events' and 'smoke incidents' so many airline staff, and passengers too, have described. It's obvious from the design of the air intake system – and from the fact that there are not many alternative culprits up there at several thousand feet – that the fumes are made up of vaporized oil components.

As we have seen, in many aircraft that have been in service since the 1960s (and are still in service today), the cabin and cockpit are supplied with bleed air that has been in close proximity to the engine lubricants. Seals such as those that are supposed to separate the lubricants from the bleed air can leak in any of three ways. The first is by design, in order to cool the seal; the second is through wear and tear, and the third is through eventual seal failure. The aerospace industry is alone in using only a single seal, where other industries use two or three seals in a row.

Some of the additives in engine oil are among the most toxic synthetic chemicals ever produced. Many of these fall into the chemical class known as organophosphates. These were originally developed as chemical warfare agents. They act to inhibit blood cholinesterase activity, which means in simple terms that they can cause continual and uncontrolled stimulation of the body's organs and muscles. Organophosphate chemical weapons include Sarin, perhaps most notoriously used in a terrorist attack in the Tokyo Metro in 1995.

Organophosphates are also used as insecticides. The toxicity which was designed into them is useful for killing bugs, but represents a major problem for the human handlers. There was a particular problem in the United Kingdom in the 1980s and 1990s that became known as 'sheep-dip syndrome'. Those farmers dipping sheep into insecticide mixtures (something farmers were legally required to do at that time) found it extremely difficult to keep clear of the mixture themselves, even if they wore protective clothing, as the sheep thrashed around and the mixture splashed accordingly. Farm workers affected by this syndrome (who showed much the same symptoms as the aircrew and passengers I have described as suffering from aerotoxic syndrome) faced a long battle – not fully won even today – to get the illness accepted and acknowledgement that their problems were caused by these chemicals, that they were not personally at fault or careless, and that they should be compensated properly for the problems caused by these work-related conditions.

More ethically acceptable uses of organophosphates than the original one as a chemical killer are as an anti-wear additive and flame retardant, and it is for these purposes that typically around 3 to 5 per cent of aviation jet engine oil is made up of organophosphate chemicals.[2] The specific chemicals commonly added to oil include different isomers of tricresyl phosphate (TCP). Isomers are variants of a chemical with slightly different molecular structures but the same chemical formula. You'll recall that this is the substance that was found on Don's shirt after he had worn it on an airliner. That test along with many others effectively proves that TCP gets into the interior atmosphere of aircraft.

The reverse side of this can of Mobil Jet 2 (engine oil) reads: 'WARNING! – Contains Tricresyl Phosphate – Prolonged or repeated breathing of oil mist, or prolonged or repeated skin contact can cause nervous system effects.' It does exactly what it says on the tin. (Since 2009 Mobil has not shown such health warnings.)

(Photographer unknown.)

In summary, organophosphates are great for engines, but very much the opposite for humans. That organophosphates are toxic and cause major health problems is not news. It has been known since they were first developed. There is a range of symptoms of organophosphate poisoning, depending on the intensity of the victim's exposure to the chemical, and on the person's individual susceptibility. Sometimes indeed there are no noticeable symptoms. A government-sponsored study at the Institute of Occupational Medicine of farmers who regularly handled organophosphates but had not complained of health problems showed that many of them suffered from mild brain damage.[3] They had a reduced ability to think clearly and solve problems. The consequences are not much fun for a farmer; you might well think it's even less amusing when it affects the pilot who is flying your airliner.

Cases of mild poisoning – what has been described as 'sheep-dip flu' in the agricultural sector – reveal symptoms more like influenza.[4] Sufferers complain of headaches, feel unusually tired, or find they can't think clearly. After a few hours, or at most a few days, those who have not been re-exposed to the poisonous substance usually recover completely. Often they do not realize they have been poisoned at all, but just imagine they have had an 'off day' or are particularly tired after a hard day's work. This too is a condition that will ring a bell with many aircrew.

Continuing exposure leads to continuing, and changing, symptoms. Among these is muscular weakness, often in the shoulder, neck and upper leg muscles. Again, these upsetting but quite diffuse symptoms often do not signal to sufferers (or to their doctors) that poisoning is the cause. And if the exposure continues over the long term, chronic effects can develop, at least in some susceptible individuals. We're talking here about the kind of chronic fatigue, aches and pains and mental problems that are apparent in the case studies in this book. And not least, they are familiar to me from my own experience. I'll explain a little of that next.

7

Not waving but wading

It was weird: the ceiling lights seemed to be moving around above my head. The goods on the shelves were moving around too. I was not on a ship or in the air; this was on the solid ground of a supermarket in Cologne, Germany. It was like a particularly strange dream or a surrealist movie, full of shifting shapes and colours. I felt dizzy and confused, and I was sweating profusely.

I staggered out of the supermarket and into the sunlight, gasping for air. I had only had a couple of beers the night before, and I couldn't think what had caused this sudden change in my health. Although I felt disoriented, I managed to make it back to my hotel. All I could think of doing was to drink as much orange juice as possible – which seemed to make me sweat even more.

It was the spring of 1990, and I was about six months into a new job flying freight aircraft, BAe 146s, all over Europe for the overnight parcel delivery company TNT. How had I come to this point in my life? I'd been dotty about flying since the age

A British Aerospace 146 300 series, operated by TNT
Source: http://www.airliners.net/photo/TNT/British-Aerospace-BAe-146-300QT/0207933/L/ Photo copyright Torsten Maiwald.

John Hoyte as an aerial crop-spraying pilot in the 1980s

of 4. De Havilland Tiger Moth crop spraying aircraft had been a particular passion, as my father worked as a salesman for a local aerial crop spraying company, but frustratingly not as a pilot.

After failing to get good enough grades at school, I was disappointed not to be able to fulfil my ambition to join the Royal Air Force (RAF). I managed to make up for that by studying and passing aeronautical exams during my first job, as a gas measurement officer, checking North Sea gas at Phillips Petroleum. Once I'd qualified as a private pilot, I then built up my flying hours as recompense for serving as the operations manager at RAF Swanton Morley, home of the Norfolk and Norwich Aero Club.

Later, I moved on to Staverton Flying School in Gloucestershire. I was a flying instructor for two years, then moved onto aerial crop spraying and aerial fire fighting. (The safety precautions were very thorough, and I never felt even slightly sick during those years.) I did this type of work in the United Kingdom, Kenya and South Australia until 1987.

I needed to progress in my career, as I had married and had a family, so I looked for a more secure and safer type of flying. I passed my Instrument Rating, which enabled me to fly in 'weather', and I took a job for two years flying DC3s, Cessna twins, on ad hoc day and night freight transporting. I also flew maritime pollution patrol aircraft to the Piper Alpha oil rig disaster and other interesting offshore incidents for Air Atlantique.

In 1989 I was glad to secure a job with an established carrier on BAe 146 aircraft with four jet engines. This represented a very large career leap for me.

In every way, my life was good at this time. I had a lovely wife and a new baby, great job, generous salary with pension and private health insurance. I should have felt like I was walking on water. Instead, it felt as though I was wading through treacle, and from time to time sinking right down into it.

In short, I felt seriously ill. The symptoms, though disturbing, were vague and erratic. I couldn't think of any obvious ailment they pointed to. I was on permanent night flying, which leads to disturbed sleep patterns, so I logically reasoned that night flying was the cause, although I had previously done a year of both day and night flying on DC3 Dakotas with no health problems.

My boarding school background had drummed into me never to complain and to be stoic, so I did not seek medical help or tell a soul. In retrospect, that was a big mistake.

I continued working for TNT for eight years, flying the BAe 146s throughout. Night shifts were not ideal, but I loved the flying, the teamwork, the BAe 146 was fun to handle, and we had highly responsible jobs. One of my favourite tasks was transporting racehorses, a specialism in itself. I flew *Istabraq* to Bristol in 1998 for the Cheltenham Festival; that was memorable as the grooms commented that they 'hadn't realized we had landed' before the champion went on to win – again. And once one of the two geldings on board attempted to get out of his stall while we were at 25,000 feet. He put his hoof clean through the marine plywood. The aircraft pitched wildly over Brussels while we pilots had to guess what was going on behind us. Even though we couldn't see the groom's battle with the horse it was our responsibility to get us down safely, and that was fine by me.

The symptoms I'd first experienced in the Cologne supermarket did not go away, though. In fact they intensified. So I learned to live with them. I would struggle through the working schedule, then on days off I would be shattered, sleeping for most of the time. I was struggling to keep going, and I soon began to turn down invitations to join other pilots for a meal or a drink as I already felt permanently inebriated and alcohol just made it twice as bad. Simple conversations were becoming embarrassing on account of my jumbled speech. I was grumpy and not good company for my wife and family either. Other pilots would later talk about being in a 'vegetable state', and that's exactly how I felt.

As the years went by my condition deteriorated further. A permanent echo started up in my head and my speech became disturbed. I could no longer pronounce certain words; they came out as a scrambled mess. I couldn't process information in noisy environments such as pubs and bars, and I struggled with conversations, even though my hearing was – and still is – near perfect.

In spite of a long list of seemingly random neurological symptoms, I always passed the regular flying medicals with ease. I chose not to tell the doctors about my problems. It seemed to me that if I did, it could only bring down more problems on me, which would jeopardize what I still felt on balance was a wonderful lifestyle.

Of course, I asked myself what could be wrong. Around 1993/94 I became convinced I had developed early-onset dementia. I also wondered if I had contracted variant Creutzfeldt–Jakob disease (vCJD) from eating too much beef, but my symptoms didn't quite match up. In fact, they didn't correspond with anything I knew about. Organophosphate poisoning was certainly not a possibility that occurred to me.

As the years passed, and I continued to fly, my mystery illness became my major preoccupation. It reached the stage where I could barely speak coherently. This is not easy for anyone, but it is particularly difficult for an airline pilot, since the job calls for continuous communication with other people. My memory was impaired too, but somehow I was able to muddle through, flying by numbers and following checklists. The emergency checks became a real problem, even though there were only about twenty short 'memory items' (such as what to do in the event of an engine failure or a fire) that I had to remember. The habits of routine flying were deeply ingrained, and I pushed on almost as a hamster runs round its wheel.

Around 1997 I flew up to Oslo Fornebu airport on a regular TNT night run. As usual I retired to the hotel room near the airport absolutely exhausted. When I went to the loo I was shocked to find the whole bowl filling with crimson blood. I didn't otherwise feel worse than usual. I cleaned up and wondered what to do. I went to bed and slept deeply.

Perhaps at that point – perhaps at many points – I should have told my colleagues and doctors, but there always seemed a good reason not to. I had already put up with much ill health without telling a soul – and if I were to go sick, who would fly the aircraft out in the evening? I was proud of having a near-perfect attendance and health record. I didn't even tell my first officer before we flew out of Fornebu that evening. The bleeding disappeared just as quickly as it had started over the next few days, only to return about two years later.

By 1998 I was in such a serious state that I was ready to quit night flying, which I blamed – perhaps in part correctly – for my health problems. But I still hesitated to get medical help. How could I describe such diffuse symptoms? Would I be believed? Anyway, I wasn't qualified for any other job. By then we had two young children and had recently moved to a larger house. Airline pilots are relatively well paid, and I couldn't face the thought of managing all of the lifestyle changes that a career switch would entail.

So I was part of what I now realize was a silent epidemic. There are many accounts in this book – and countless others in archives globally – of aircrew who have reached the point of telling others about the health problems they were experiencing. But for much the same reasons that I delayed so long myself, I am sure there are many more who struggle on with their jobs, fearful of the outcome if they tell anyone at all.

8

The tombstone imperative

I took the initiative a while ago to contact an aviation journalist, Andy Weir, author of *The Tombstone Imperative,* to tell him of the day-to-day reality of working for low-cost airlines. The colourful phrase in the title of his book, first published by Simon & Schuster in 1999, comes from the industry's tendency to wait for 'tombstones' before correcting an apparent safety weakness. In other words, problems are not taken seriously unless and until they lead to a significant number of deaths.

Here is an example he cites. In July 1988, pilots in an Airbus A320 programmed their flight computer for descent on an angle of 3 degrees, but forgot to turn one small knob, so the computer interpreted this as an ultra-fast descent of 3,000 feet per minute. The crew responded and corrected just in time.

The same error occurred in January 1992 on an approach into Strasbourg, in poor weather, and this time the crew responded too late. Nearly everyone on board was killed as the aircraft hit a mountainside. Only after this second incident was the A320 display amended.[1]

In-flight fume events have also come within a few seconds of creating dozens of tombstones. One incident occurred on 12 November 1999 in the skies near Malmo, Sweden. I describe it in detail in Chapter 20. Some other incidents are summarized in Chapter 14.

9

The size of the problem

As we shall see repeatedly in this book, it is often claimed that fume events are not a serious problem, and one reason given for this is that they are rare. So it's worth considering exactly how rare they are.

The UK government has estimated the incidence of serious fume events as 0.05 per cent of flights, which sounds like a tiny number. But in 2012 there were 37.5 million flights worldwide, according to the International Air Transport Association (IATA).[1] At a rate of 0.05 per cent, that would mean there were fume events on 18,750 flights, or around fifty every day. (And it's worth stressing that there is some presence of toxic chemicals in the aircraft air even when no identifiable 'fume event' has happened, all the time that the aircraft engine is running – and that even this tiny proportion can be harmful to health.)

It does not necessarily follow, however, that this proportion of fume events are found in research studies of the problem. Most research takes place in controlled circumstances: a selection of flights are chosen for monitoring in advance (we'll see that, for example, in the discussion of the Cranfield research study: see Chapter 33). If an airline has agreed for one or more of its aircraft to be the subject of a research study, that aircraft is likely to receive maintenance of a higher standard than a typical aircraft used by a low-cost airline during the holiday season.

It's a familiar problem, much appreciated by scientific and social-scientific researchers, that to observe something inevitably changes it. This is not to imply bad faith on the part of the researchers or the airline, it's more an unavoidable aspect of the research design. Similarly, we tend to take more care in driving a car when taking a test than when we are late for an important meeting. But it's a problem that needs to be borne in mind when extrapolating from the research results. Until detectors are fitted the size of the problem will remain aviation's 'inconvenient truth'.

10

Symptoms and syndromes

The notions of diseases and their causes are so fundamental to our concept of medicine today that it can be quite surprising to realize it wasn't always so.

In the medieval era, doctors thought in terms of humours. The balance of black bile, yellow bile, phlegm and blood determined both a person's temperament and their health, and the solution to health problems, the doctors believed, was to try to alter the balance of the humours. Only much later did people realize how wrong they were.

Then came the famous developments that shaped later generations of medicine: the discoveries of bacteria and viruses, the realization of their role in causing diseases, and the development of antibiotics and vaccinations. If people today put great store by receiving a diagnosis, it's surely in no small part because we know that a diagnosis of a disease such as smallpox can lead to the identification of a good treatment. If you don't know what's wrong with you, how can you be treated successfully for it? Any treatment you get will be as much trial and error as the bloodletting of those earlier eras.

Today, people find consolation even in the diagnosis of conditions for which there are no known cures. We like to put labels on things, if only to explain to others what's wrong with us. Parents of children who are bright, inclined to strong compulsions and find social interaction difficult sigh with relief when it's confirmed they have Asperger's syndrome, even though nobody really knows how to alleviate that condition. A diagnosis such as chronic fatigue syndrome offers – superficially, at least – much the same kind of assurance. At least they know what's wrong with me now, the sufferers often think to themselves.

There is, though, a real difference between a disease such as smallpox or chickenpox, and a syndrome such as Asperger's syndrome, or indeed chronic fatigue syndrome. Doctors and scientists are pretty clear what causes chickenpox. It's defined by infection with the *varicellazoster* virus (VZV), it has a known course, and the treatment is tested and proven. A 'syndrome', on the other hand, is just a name for a set of symptoms. They occur together frequently enough that it is worth giving a specific name to the combination of symptoms, but that doesn't mean there is a common factor that brings them on in all cases, let alone that medicine has identified it and worked out successful treatments for it.

It is important to bear this in mind. Because when doctors give a patient a label such as 'chronic fatigue syndrome' they are not, in fact, diagnosing a disease. They are just putting an accepted label on a set of symptoms. Even if the label is the correct one, it doesn't tell us any more about what caused the syndrome, or how – if at all – it can be cured. This is also true of aerotoxic syndrome.

This is particularly important to remember when it's suggested to patients that their condition is a psychosomatic one: that is, it is 'all in the mind'. That's an absolute statement in a world that in reality is much more relative, of course. It's a truism that the mind and body are so interlinked that nothing is genuinely all in the mind, or all in the body come to that; we just can't separate the two in such a simplistic way. But it's a truism that has practical effect when doctors select a course of treatment. If they think a condition is mentally induced (which does not necessarily mean that it was consciously brought on by the patient; that's rarely the implication), they will probably advise a completely different treatment than if they think the symptoms were, for instance, caused by chemical poisoning.

Even psychiatrists treating patients with accepted (and named) mental illnesses cannot agree to what extent mind-based treatments such as therapy or more physically oriented treatments such as drugs are appropriate. And practitioners, both general and specialist, who treat patients with fatigue and neurological symptoms don't agree either. But a proportion of them – in my experience, a very sizeable proportion – work on the hypothesis that the condition is psychosomatic, and they prescribe treatment on that basis.

So let's be clear. That an illness is psychosomatic is not something that can ever be proven. It is at best a hypothesis. It means that the practitioner has identified no other cause.

It doesn't mean they *know* there is no other cause. And if they prescribe treatment on the assumption that the disease is a psychosomatic one, then they are effectively indulging in guesswork (or choice, if you prefer) on two different levels. First, they are guessing at a cause when they do not honestly know what the cause is. And second, they are guessing at a treatment when by and large, there is no consensus on what the best treatment might be.

A lot of airline staff with aerotoxic syndrome have experienced this situation. Let's look next at a couple of their accounts.

11

All in the mind?

Miraculous escapes and horrific incarceration

This is the story of Len Lawrence, a pilot who was right to fear admitting to his physical symptoms. The saga that followed lost him his wife, home, liberty and personal assets.

Len not only experienced fume events, he recorded them, so there can be no question that they occurred. The first he recorded was on 29 November 1991. He was co-pilot on an aircraft that had passed V1 (the speed at which the aircraft is committed to becoming airborne) during its takeoff run when the flight deck suddenly filled with hot acrid fumes. Both he and his captain were blinded by them. They could neither see outside the cockpit nor see the instruments clearly. Their skin was burning and they found it difficult to breathe. And at the same time they were accelerating in excess of 160 mph. They put on their oxygen masks, started their emergency drill and warned Air Traffic Control that they were in an emergency situation.

Fortunately the captain was a highly experienced pilot with many years' experience of the aircraft model they were flying. He had to feel his way along the instrument panel to locate the dump valve, which effectively lets air out of the aircraft. Within about three seconds the fumes cleared. The whole fume incident had lasted for about 15 seconds. The aircraft then made an emergency landing and all on board were evacuated.

Len's last recorded fume event occurred in 2004. The handling pilot was a recently retired UK Civil Aviation Authority (CAA) flight operation inspector, so he could hardly have been more distinguished or experienced in his profession. He and Len, his co-pilot, noticed an oily smell on the flight deck. Len still can't understand exactly what happened, but he knows that the aircraft descended to less than 500 feet above the city of Amsterdam. The only time it is ever safe to be this low is during takeoff and landing, but the pilots had not just taken off and were not planning to land. Although Len wasn't actually flying the aircraft, it worries him greatly that he failed to intervene promptly and ensure the pilot corrected the course. Both men were still thoroughly confused when they eventually instigated a climb to 1,500 feet.

The next day the same two men were flying the aircraft to Italy, when Swiss air traffic control gave them an instruction to reroute over Switzerland. As Len puts it:

> Both the captain and I were unable to process the information being given. That was my last ever flight before I resigned. Why did I resign? Because I could not, and indeed still cannot, think clearly enough to fly.

You might well think Len was lucky to still be alive, and not to have killed anyone else. But he certainly wasn't lucky in what followed. Although evidence of the effects of breathing toxic fumes was made known to the psychiatrists to whom he was referred, they chose not to consider this option, and instead to diagnose him with a mental illness. Solicitors who became involved also failed to suggest this alternative explanation. Len was effectively 'held captive' as a mental patient for almost eighteen months, heavily medicated, during which time most of his assets were disposed of. At last, the fifth psychiatrist he was seen by reviewed the evidence, and he was referred for specialist treatment for poisoning by a substance that had been identified as tricresyl phosphate.

A stewardess's story

Dee Passon, who worked as cabin crew for twenty-five years, nineteen of them at British Airways, gave the following interview for this book. Dee has waived patient confidentiality and supplied me with copies of letters from a BA doctor and her general practitioner. She had breast cancer in 2005, three years before she was diagnosed with aerotoxic syndrome, but this was diagnosed early and treated successfully. She feels that her working environment may also have been a contributory factor to the cancer.

'For a long time I would ask myself, why am I so unlucky? I had a cough. I had chest X-rays that showed nothing. 2002 was the last year I felt well. In the winter 2002/03 I had constant flu-like symptoms. I was shaving my arms, and had aches under the arms. I went to the doctor, and she found that all the glands were swollen. They thought it was glandular fever. I had three tests – all negative. I continued to feel dreadful, but thought that I had never bounced back from the glandular fever. I had sweats; the doctor said it was the menopause. But I also had terrible pains in my arms – I later found out this was caused by peripheral nerve damage.

'I have a report from Professor Abou-Donia[1] that says I have severe nervous system damage. I had high blood pressure, and no reflexes down my left side. I was anaemic – low red blood cell count, for no apparent reason. I was eating healthily, didn't smoke.

'The next thing, in 2003 there was a fume event I think. At the time I didn't know fume events existed. We had a flight in 2004, and so many passengers and crew were ill: on the flight deck, they checked the pressurization, and it was fine. It was only when one crew member collapsed that it was agreed to do a flight report. I can remember, on that flight I had pins and needles. My lips were blue. I asked the guys at the back, how are you feeling? They said "The same." One passenger was screaming abuse at her husband. I had to get someone to remind me how to do the oxygen mask [for her]. I had been flying for twenty years but I couldn't remember. For years, on lots of flights other people were ill and I wasn't, so I don't think I'm genetically susceptible but gradually my ability to detoxify became impaired.

'On one B767 flight, people were projectile vomiting in the aisles. I went round talking to the passengers. There was no common denominator: some had eaten, some hadn't. I did a report. The only thing they all had was the water on the plane. So I requested a test done on that. They didn't do that test. I managed to pull out that report from BA files. They had edited it completely. They took out the bits about not having eaten. They were making it sound like air [travel] sickness. It had been stamped "No further investigation required". I'm pretty sure that flight had contaminated air.

'Then I got pneumonia. On day six of antibiotics I was

scared to go to bed because my lungs were barely working and I thought that if I lay down I might die. We didn't know it was chemical.

'It was like looking at the world through a cracked pane of glass: everything was distorted. There was a disconnect from reality. Nothing was making sense. My driving was all over the place. I didn't understand why until I read Dr Myhill's[2] observation that the eye sees things that the brain doesn't. I saw things coming towards me, and was asking myself: Is that a car? I was reluctant to agree to go back to work. I only went back for five trips after the pneumonia. When your body has had enough, it doesn't matter how much you love your job. I thought it would go away when I gave up flying, but every time I get anti-bacterial spray in a restaurant or go near air freshener it comes back.

'I went back reluctantly after the pneumonia. I thought, I can't continue to be this unlucky. I did a flight to Phoenix. I had migraine, headache and vomiting for twelve hours. Made it to the flight home. Unlocked the car in the car park and my right arm just wouldn't work. Fortunately I have an automatic. I got home, tried to make a cup of tea, and I dropped the kettle. I sat down and just started crying. I knew it was neurological.

'The doctor was completely mystified why I was going downhill. He was lovely – very supportive – he never thought it was just something in my head.

'I went to Cape Town. The smoke detector went off in the toilet on landing – for no apparent reason. The official reason was "condensation". I think it was fumes. The next day the purser didn't turn up [because of sickness].

'One doctor said, yes ... this is organophosphate poisoning. He put aerotoxic syndrome on my diagnosis. Of course, BA hated that. They tried to tell me it was all in my head. I started putting it [this term] in online forums. Every person was told: "You're the only one."

'I compiled a list of thirty-six crew members who had died in a thirty-four-month period. I asked a BA doctor [in a letter]: "One crew member a month dying: do you think there's a problem?" After my letter about all the deaths I got a phone call from my manager, asking me to see her. This was less than two weeks after the letter. I took my union representative. The BA doctor had said that I could work on the ground in six months' time. I was expecting us to agree a date [at that meeting]. But she told me "I'm giving you three months' notice from today." The union rep said "Are you sacking her?" She couldn't look me in the eye. I knew it [the order] wasn't from her.

'I couldn't afford to [take BA to an industrial tribunal]. I saw a guy in Crawley who took £1,100 off me. But I had income protection insurance, which paid out. Now I had lost my job. My insurance company sent me to an independent expert, Dr Jenny Goodman. She was brilliant. She said it was definitely aerotoxic syndrome. BA are still trying to make out that it doesn't exist.

'I have a letter sent by the BA doctor to my GP. It was the best thing BA could have done. It says there are tests available, but we don't advise to send your patient for them, because they are invasive. My GP responded "How dare BA tell me how to treat my patient?" That got him on my side. He was really supportive after that. This just shows that the reason they don't know [about aerotoxic syndrome] is because they're not looking for anything.

'I was lucky to have a supportive doctor. Otherwise, I might not be here today.'

Deanne Wientge – testimony of a former US flight attendant

'In September 2010 I went off a plane by ambulance along with three other flight attendants after helping investigate the source of a strong chemical smell, as it filled the aircraft cabin. I was on my way to work as a flight attendant for a large North American airline when a smell I can only describe as a dirty sock mixed with chemical smell suddenly permeated the entire plane, literally causing me to jump up off the jump seat in alarm and exclaim to the flight attendant next to me, "What is that?" As I was flying non-revenue and as all seats were full, I was assigned to the jump seat in the rear of the plane.

'The other flight attendant and I immediately checked the three rear lavatories for the source of the smell, and then asked the passengers in the rear seats if they could smell it. They said "Yes."

'We moved forward towards the front of the plane. I noted that there seemed to be pockets of the smell throughout the plane. As we approached the forward galley, the alarm bells in my head were skyrocketing, for I knew immediately something was dreadfully wrong. The smell seemed strongest there. Later I was to find out that the pilots could also detect the smell throughout the flight deck. (I have no knowledge of if the pilots developed any symptoms though, or whether they donned their oxygen masks during the flight.) The forward flight attendant told us, "I know this smell. I've been through it before. Put wet paper towels over your mouth and sit down", which one of the flight attendants promptly did. While I never saw a visible mist, in hindsight I realized that the hues of colour were not what they should have been. Two things went through my head. Firstly, is this a chemical attack, is a passenger using chemicals? Secondly, I need to get to the rear of the aircraft and make sure it is not left unattended. You see, I was fairly new to flying and knew nothing of "air quality events" or what they smell like.

'The other three flight attendants talked in the forward galley, trying to determine the source of the smell, as the fourth remained seated. Good thing that she did, as she ended up being the only one of us who was not incapacitated. By the time the other flight attendants returned to the rear of the aircraft, two of them were assisting the third who was having difficulty walking. To me she appeared to have an ash-grey pallor and her eyes had a distinctly yellowish cast that she had not previously had. We did our best to prepare for landing. The second flight attendant began vomiting repeatedly when she tried to do the landing announcements. It was becoming harder and harder to breathe and think. I remember a burning sensation in my chest. The three of us donned the oxygen masks on a three-port portable oxygen bottle. It was immediately easier to breathe. Watching the other two I feared they would not be upright much longer and said, "I'm calling the captain."

The captain could not respond at that time as I believe we were still on the active taxiway and I believe he was on the phone with the forward flight attendant. When the captain responded that he could not answer, all I could think to do was sit sideways as we taxied in, watch the flight deck door and watch the four flight attendants and passengers to make sure all remained upright. I did not know that one of the forward flight attendants who had been up and about the cabin was also incapacitated to the point that she told the one sitting that she was unable to help with de-boarding and placed herself on oxygen. I could not complete the simple task of getting the gloves out of the bag on my lap and wondered why.

'When we arrived at the gate the passengers were asked to remain seated so the paramedics could get to us. I do not understand medical jargon but was fairly certain that the paramedics commented to each other that the two flight attendants next to me had abnormal vitals. Both were later decontaminated at the hospital, though I was not despite having been next to them the whole time.

'As we got to the front of the plane I remember that the few remaining passengers to deplane were complaining to the pilots about the smell. The paramedics were working on the lead flight attendant in the first class seats who looked very ill. Her eyes only half open, I heard her whisper to them haltingly "get ... us ... off ... this ... plane", at which point the paramedics nodded in agreement and moved us to the jetbridge to continue their evaluation. The lead flight attendant later told me that at that point she had felt barely conscious and that that was not her first fume event, but her fourth! I tried to explain to the pilots as I got to them, "I don't know what but something is very, very wrong on this plane. That was no ordinary odour." I remember trying to tell the paramedics as I stood on the jetbridge and they worked on the other two who had been next to me on gurneys that I felt like my heart was beating out of my chest and I was shaking terribly.

The emergency room

'At the ER, I was promptly placed in a room and left. Later I received an email from the other two who were next to me, telling me that in the ER, they had been put in decontamination showers immediately, had blood taken, blood gases and IV fluids. The e-mail from one of them says that they both exhibited a very delayed response when given a finger test by the ER doctor and that all of us had similar signs of confusion, dizziness, headache and nausea. All of us would go on to describe feeling shaky in the days to come, except for the one who had remained seated. The ambulance driver returned with my bags and asked why I had taken off my oxygen mask. I held up the end of the tube and said "because it's not hooked up".

I waited alone for a long time. The supervisor who had met the plane arrived and asked the hospital where I was. They seemed to have trouble finding me, she said. I waited longer for them to find me a room. When the doctor finally saw me, my company supervisor was in the room taking notes. The doctor started by telling me that they would not be doing any medical tests on me because they would come back negative and there was nothing that it would show. He told me they had already checked the others. He then started asking me my medical history, at which point I looked over at my supervisor, knowing full well that it was a clear violation of HIPPA privacy laws for her to be in the room. Seeing that she was writing, I stopped answering the doctor's questions and simply looked from him over to her. She left. The doctor gave me some discharge papers that read simply "Inhalation Exposure" and "Dizziness".

Post event

'The next few days I was extremely fatigued and unable to stay up long. I called in sick and slept for two days. After trying to stand for two hours on the second day, I had to lie back down and sleep. I was pale and had a severe headache. I had burning of my eyes, throat and sinuses which lasted for weeks. At that point I knew I needed a doctor, and called someone on our company assistance card to ask for help in finding one. I really don't recall much of my conversation with her. I remember calling another flight attendant but I have no idea what I said to him or what he said back. My notes are all illegible. On Sunday I tried to go to church. I was too fatigued to stand up and sat down. I remained seated the entire service. I returned home to bed and sleep.

'It was about that time that I learned of fume events, aerotoxic syndrome and also about a research project being done through the University of Washington. Knowing something bad had happened on that plane I was eager to get to the bottom of it, and more than happy to donate my blood for the research. On Monday, I drove down to the university where I gave blood for the study and learned more about the research from the biochemist. I remember being distinctly pale and fatigued as I walked from the parking lot into the university. It seemed to me that for days and weeks after that my skin and eyes had a sickly, yellow cast. I have a photo that to me still shows it. I also seemed to have great difficulty regulating body temperature and felt cold all of the time. Some days my palms had a purplish cast to them, and even now they are rarely warm to the touch. There were days I would take up to seven showers a day just to get warm. For probably a year after that I knew there was no way I could return to doing my volunteer Search & Rescue work as I got cold much too easily, and sitting in the wilderness waiting for dogs to find me as part of the training exercise was out of the question. I was also much too easily fatigued to trek up mountains.

'Three days after my exposure I went to the walk-in clinic because of the burning in my chest, lungs and sinuses in addition to the extreme fatigue. The doctor's diagnosis was toxic fume inhalation. He cleared me to fly and told me to keep my appointment I already had scheduled. I found a doctor who specialized in chemical inhalation in my area and I already had an appointment for the following Wednesday. When I arrived at the appointment, I was told that the doctor could not see me as they only take workman's compensation cases. My workman's compensation was initially denied and was not reversed until three months later by request of the company.

'It was some time during the week after the event that the tremors began. Prior to the day of the event, I had never had tremors of the hands, arms or neck. As I recall they were at first just in my hands. Later they would develop in my arms, neck and come to involve other parts of my body at times. At times you can see my whole arm shaking and a purplish cast on one of my palms. A video was taken on 4 January, three months after my exposure. I consider this video as quite personal and it is with trepidation that I share it with you now, but for the others who are affected even worse than I and in hopes that no others should have to ever experience it.

'After three more months of flying I was having difficulty walking too. I'm not sure when, how or why it started, but my left arm I held close to my body for many weeks after the event. Something about keeping it rigidly against my body prevented it from shaking. The more I relaxed my muscles at times the worse the tremors were, though I could be doing anything when the tremors began, such as pouring a soda or resting my head on someone's arm while watching a movie.

'The doctors having said I was cleared to fly, I had no choice but to return to flying or accumulate points and lose my job. My first flight back the following week put me on a trip with many short hops, requiring multiple boardings, de-boardings and announcements. Each service had to be done rapidly. I immediately noticed several things. I would reach for things and be unable to remember what I was reaching for. Though I knew the announcements by heart I could not remember them. I went to read them and found it very difficult. I could see the words on the page but not process them. It seemed to me a long delay before I could say each word. It improved over time but my cognitive processing is clearly not what it was, nor am I able to focus very well. Once an avid reader, I find it much harder to focus on what I read or write. My handwriting worsened. Even now I find myself having to stop to distinguish words such as "hear" for "here" and "no" for "know", often finding that I wrote the wrong one. That was not something I had experienced prior to the event. In fact, in graduate school I had a 4.0 out of 4.0 grade point average because I could write well and was elected to the Jesuit National Honour Society based on a number of merits. I now have greater difficulty with cognition and memory since the incident.

The doctors

'While visiting my family I received a phone call from the workman's compensation claims administrator informing me I was to see their doctor. I was later to find out that the doctor they sent me to was the former manager of occupational medicine programmes for one of, if not the, largest airline manufacturers in the world. I also learned that he had been the key expert witness for the defence in an aerotoxic case that was lost due to being blamed on mass hysteria. One lawyer I spoke with told me that that particular case was a travesty of justice. This doctor's report on my condition includes the following statement: "She provides a story of other flight attendants being treated somewhat heroically with decontamination."

'According to one article I found recently, this same doctor that I was sent to is one of the nine doctors that sit on a panel of doctors who have formed a regional organization of occupational and environmental medicine working in conjunction with this state's medical association, and in fact they share the same office and the same phone number. The doctor I was sent to is quoted as saying when asked what the association does that its members are on the side of science and not on the side of advocacy for certain types of exposure as legitimate medical claims. The article asserts that state records for the panel indicate that the registered agent for the organization is one of the largest law firms locally, with the airline being one of its biggest clients, and it defended the airline in a case filed by flight attendants who had become mysteriously ill from working inside the airline's planes.

'The doctor who sits on that panel went so far in his report as to say, "She was returned to work and continued to work for four months during which time she apparently did a lot of research on aerotoxic syndrome." When I think back to the events that happened on that plane and the post effects, there is no shadow of a doubt in my head that I did not make up my illness or tremors, nor am I, nor was I ever, a malingerer or hypochondriac. Validation and scientific tests confirming and backing up our tests are crucial to peace of mind. I applaud the doctors, biochemists, and advocates around the world who are working hard to do just that. Aerotoxic syndrome as a result of exposure to chemicals in jet aircraft is both real and debilitating.'

12

The airline response

We have already seen something of how airlines, and the doctors and lawyers who work for them, respond to staff (and passengers) who report health problems that fit what we describe here as aerotoxic syndrome. But let's look a little more at what typically happens, and just as importantly, why it does so.

It's no surprise to any of us that managements in all industries are reluctant to accept responsibility for health problems that arise as a result of their operations. If they admit responsibility for even one case, they are setting precedents for other cases. And in an environment where the emphasis is put on corporate profit, and corporate social responsibility is more buzzword than reality, no single company can afford to do that.

One of the lawyers I talked to about compensation for my own health problems put this very clearly. At first he reckoned that my case was straightforward enough that he would be able to get me a payout on the basis of industrial injury, but then as he faced entrenched corporate opposition (and battalions of lawyers on the opposition benches), and considered the timescale, he began to backtrack rapidly. He said that proving beyond doubt – although in fact only 'on the balance of probability' is required – that my chronic illness had been caused by jet aircraft was almost impossible, as proving 'causation' would always be difficult.

It would not seem so difficult to prove that organophosphates are poisonous, as insect killing was their original intended use. Anyway, as I have pointed out, it was not as if my case was unique. It is always hard to put an exact number on how many other aircrew have also suffered from similar symptoms. If it was accepted that these symptoms were caused by toxic fumes – and particularly if it was accepted that the airlines were at fault in having let the toxic incidents continue when they could have done more to prevent them – then all the other affected crew and passengers would also be in a position to claim compensation. As my lawyer put it, 'There isn't enough money in the world to recompense everyone.' That was perhaps an exaggeration, but there certainly isn't enough money for airlines to compensate everyone and continue to operate profitably.

Another accepted fact is that what aircrew experience, so do passengers. If fit and healthy aircrew were able to get it accepted that oil fumes had brought them to their knees, what would be the effect on others, particularly children and other vulnerable groups? Many of them would have even more cause for complaint. However, these people typically never know what caused their ill health.

Aircrew reporting health problems rarely find a warm and sympathetic reception. They often feel they are being blamed themselves, even when they are convinced the problem arises from their working conditions. As we have seen, the tendency to label them with chronic fatigue syndrome (which suggests, if only subliminally, that they are not really ill, but only extremely tired) and to attribute a psychosomatic cause to it (which suggests that the fault is in their minds, even if it's not in their conscious minds) tends to reinforce this. It works to shift the perceived blame from the employer to the individual employee (or the individual passenger).

There is a great deal of pressure placed on airline management, particularly in the current highly competitive environment, and this is reflected in issues such as the intensification of rosters and the reduction of aircraft turnaround times. These issues put pressure on aircrew in their turn. So even if 'stress' and 'burnout' are sometimes wrongly applied as labels when 'chemical poisoning' is much more relevant, there often *is* an element of stress and burnout when an aircrew member goes off sick. Conveniently for the airlines, it's not easy to disentangle the causes when someone feels exhausted; the tiredness is real enough, even if it's magnified by the effects of the toxins. All of this makes it very difficult for a sick individual to establish a clear-cut case and win it against an industry determined to prevent them from doing so.

For many aircrew, exhausted both by their illness and by long months, if not years, of battling for compensation, it is not too bad a deal if they settle for a payoff without admission of liability. As I have mentioned, it's a practice in the industry to give pilots a sizeable payment (equivalent to up to three years' wages) if they surrender their licence and end their flying career. It's understandable that some people choose to accept this kind of settlement and do not persevere.

Single, sick individuals are unsurprisingly easy meat for a well-coordinated industry which is constantly discovering 'new' diseases yet fails to recognize the self-same diseases as were identified in the 1950s.

But if individuals give in, this sets its own kind of precedent. Only by working together and by providing an overwhelming mass of evidence can we counterbalance the airline industry's allegation that aerotoxic syndrome doesn't really exist. Although a few people, passengers or employees, may make frivolous or fraudulent illness claims, those who truly do suffer this potentially debilitating injury must not be marginalized by inadequate company responses. Professional, moral and ethical considerations demand that passengers and airline employees who have been affected by contaminated cabin air be treated honestly and with sincerity.

That is why I have set up the Aerotoxic Association. But I don't pretend to be entirely blame-free here. I too experienced – and to a large extent gave in to – the urge to agree a financial settlement and put the whole thing behind me, although that was before I understood what had made me ill in the first place. Let me tell you some more of my own experience now.

13

Red alert

First, it's important to catch up from where my narrative last left me, flying BAe 146 freight aircraft. At the outset of my airline career in 1989, my ambition had been to graduate from a medium-sized aircraft like the BAe 146 to something larger, for example a Boeing 757, and fly on longer routes. That is a typical career progression for a pilot. In the late 1990s I was still only in my mid-40s, and this would have been the normal next step. But I was worried that my 'mystery illness' meant I would have serious difficulty learning to fly a new aircraft type. There is always a mass of new data, different control systems and so on to master when you start to fly a different type. I knew the BAe 146 so well that I had no problem flying it even in my poor condition, and so I decided the best idea would be to stay with the BAe 146, but to switch from the night flights, which I had thought were causing my illness, to daytime flying.

There were still a few short-haul UK carriers operating the BAe 146, and in 1998 I applied to Jersey European Airways – later to become the budget airline Flybe – and got a 'direct entry' as an experienced captain. For the next seven years I flew short-haul passenger flights, between UK airports (particularly Birmingham, Belfast and the Channel Isles) and destinations all over Europe.

I was flying on New Year's Eve 2002 when there was a serious incident on board. For the first time in my career, the emergency red call light from the cabin crew lit up in front of me. We had just begun a 'round-the-islands' trip – Birmingham–Jersey–Guernsey–Birmingham – and were still climbing on the initial Birmingham–Jersey leg when my number one, Emma, told me on the intercom. 'There's a fire in the rear toilet.' Under the circumstances she was admirably cool; she knew as well as I did that an uncontrolled fire in an aircraft creates an immensely dangerous situation.

Being provided with established procedures to follow

certainly helped me and my first officer Steve 'Bravo' to stay calm and deal with the emergency. Steve was the handling pilot for the flight, so we elected that he would continue to fly the aircraft during the descent and landing. This is a good division of labour in an emergency; the first officer flies the aircraft, while the captain analyses the situation, communicates with Air Traffic Control (ATC) and the passengers and crew, and generally manages events.

I immediately radioed a Mayday call to London and announced to the passengers that we had to make an immediate return to Birmingham. London ATC were excellent. They descended us quickly down to 2,500 feet and cleared us for landing, before handing us back to Birmingham, where the controllers already knew about our serious problem. We opted for a fast 'tear drop' approach with a slight tail wind bringing us back onto the runway we had just departed from.

Meanwhile, Emma helped the other cabin crew gather fire extinguishers and check the rear panels for heat, seeking the source of the blaze. This wasn't easy; there was plenty of smoke in the toilets, but it didn't seem to be the seat of the fire. Then, mysteriously, the smoke dissipated as we began the descent. Because the fire didn't seem to be getting worse, we decided we need not order the passengers to do a full emergency evacuation down the chutes when we reached the ground. It is not easy to use the chutes, and it can cause serious injuries to passengers, so it is good practice to do so only when essential. We were met by a full turnout of fire engines following us down the runway, and once the passengers had disembarked the fire crew came on board.

They didn't find a fire, and in retrospect it was clear that there had not been one. This had just been a particularly bad oil 'fume event'.

The company's eventual version of events was that the Number 3 engine bleed air valve was brand new and that the engineers had failed to remove the protective oil that the valve is covered in before fitting it. This oil then had apparently burned off into the cabin, so it was a small incident that would by its nature have been short-lived. I found this explanation hard to accept. There had been so much visible smoke: I thought the sheer amount of fumes indicated a more major oil leak. And there were rumours floating around the company at this time about a change in the type of oil to be used in the future, because engineering had found something unsafe.

I learned much later that the company's explanation was not in fact true. The cause of the fumes had been neat engine oil contaminating the bleed air from Number 3 engine. In early 2003, however, we were too exhausted, and busy with the schedule, to have the time or the energy to pursue the matter.

14

Incidents across the world

Here's another selection of those supposedly rare fume incidents.

The Kolver incident

This incident, which occurred in Australia, takes its name from Captain Frank Kolver, the senior pilot aboard a BAe 146 freighter when it occurred on 10 July 1997. There were just three individuals on board: a co-pilot and a supernumerary pilot in addition to Captain Kolver. While on descent into Melbourne the crew smelled oil fumes, and Captain Kolver began to experience difficulty in concentrating, and a loss of situational awareness. Shortly before landing, he handed over controls to the co-pilot, who landed safely. The other two crew members also reported symptoms, though they were less severe than the captain's. Because the fumes were not in the form of a visible mist, they did not follow the smoke-removal checklist, or use oxygen masks.

Around six hours after the incident, and for the next ten days, Captain Kolver suffered from severe headaches characterized by the feeling of a strong pressure on the top of the head. This diminished over time, but he also reported balance problems while attempting to rise in a darkened room at night, and that he had experienced increased headaches and vertigo while travelling.

After beginning the flight in Sydney, the supernumerary pilot had examined the aircraft maintenance log and saw a note of a defect, dated 17 June 1997, relating to oil residue at the number two air conditioning pack inlet, resulting from an oil leak in the number four engine. There was no indication it had been dealt with, but even so the aircraft had been cleared for flight. After shutdown at Melbourne, the crew vacated the aircraft and the fumes dissipated. They continued with further flights, but with the number 4 engine bleed air system turned off. The rest of the tour was without incident.

The pilot submitted an air safety incident report. The engine was replaced on 16 July 1997. The subsequent investigation by the Australian Transport Safety Bureau uncovered examples of flight crew from several Australian operators of BAe 146 aircraft with health problems. It concluded:

> The crew members reported that they were either off work permanently, on prolonged sick leave, or in receipt of medical certificates that precluded them from undertaking normal crew duties on the aircraft. The crew members reported a variety of differing physical reactions arising from their perceived exposure to fume contamination, the most common being sore eyes, nose and throat; nausea; tiredness; and headache. The more disabling reactions reported include any of the above symptoms plus any of the following: dizziness, balance problems, extreme tiredness, extreme reaction to all oilbased products (including plastics and cosmetics), feelings of intoxication, slurred speech, inability to walk straight, skin rash, itchiness and blotching.[1]

All of the facts in this summary come from the formal Australian government inquiry into the incident.

Captain Kolver addressed the subsequent Senate inquiry three years later. The full testimony is available via the web and is well worth a read. One excerpt runs:

> from 12 June to 10 July, oil fumes were becoming a regular occurrence, but we were not overly concerned as we had been assured by management ... that the effects of the oil fumes were not detrimental .... So the event into Melbourne on 10 July was no different from many previous occasions when we were operating the aircraft where oxygen masks were not required. It was just another event of oil odours in the cockpit, and none of the three crew on board considered it necessary to put on the oxygen masks .... it was not a situation where I became incapacitated totally. It was a recognition that I was having difficulty. According to the training we have received, I elected to hand over the operation of the aircraft to the first officer. I believe I still assisted him and

> supported him on the approach and landing .... I think I also had to taxi the aircraft in from the runway to the parking position as the steering wheel is just on the captain's side. I certainly was not hyperventilating.[2]

It is worth observing the contrast between how people sceptical about the effects of aerotoxins loudly insist on the highest levels of 'scientific evidence', and how they frequently resort to pure speculation about other possible causes of the problems aircrew experience, talking about 'hyperventilation' and the like. Professional pilots like Captain Kolver have to suffer groundless character assassination for having the temerity to give their testimony.

Some fume events in Northern Ireland

On 21 October 2007 complaints about contaminated air on ten flights between Belfast and other destinations in the United Kingdom on BAe 146 aircraft operated by Flybe resulted in a protest by cabin crew. A BBC news report confirmed that noxious fumes leaked into cabins on the Flybe flights. It added that 'During a flight from Birmingham, two stewards collapsed after being overcome by fumes. Another flight was aborted after the crew had to use oxygen masks. Staff said they were concerned about health risks. Flybe is to withdraw the aircraft concerned early next year.'

Flybe did indeed seek to reassure the public and its own staff by emphasizing that it was phasing out 146s. Its statement, which the BBC reported, read:

> Flybe is completely confident that its aircraft are operated and maintained to the highest industry standards. In line with many previous public announcements, Flybe took a commercial decision several years ago to reduce the number of aircraft types operated from three to two. As a result the BAe 146 fleet will have been withdrawn by February 2008.[3]

In July 2007, seven crew members were taken to hospital in Belfast after the stewards collapsed on a flight from Birmingham. One was off work for more than a month. Some cabin crew refused to fly any longer on the 146. One flight attendant told the BBC, 'I will not get back on the 146 again. I'm angry that my health has been put at risk.' A Flybe pilot said that if he was asked to fly the 146 he would reply 'Go take a walk.'[4]

A short while after these events I went up to Belfast to meet some of the affected crew and their families. I spoke with a family member, who told me:

> A member of my family has been flying a BAe 146 for over two years. After about seven months we began to notice a change in her. We thought this was just due to tiredness and flying long hours. Like most other people we didn't know the facts or the symptoms associated with breathing in fumes.
>
> Unfortunately we learned the hard way as she was aboard a plane that had a major incident when all the crew were affected and some actually passed out due to the fumes on board. As a family we watched a very happy bubbly person, very confident and full of life, become withdrawn, tired, irritable and lethargic. The biggest shock is the sight of a person you love coming out of casualty very pale, swaying almost like they're drunk, and they can't even remember simple things like date of birth. This was bad, but the violent sickness was terrible and lasted for days. The headaches took weeks to go away.
>
> It happened again; again crew were affected by fumes and some crew passed out. All of the symptoms she had before were exaggerated so much it was unbelievable. The sickness lasted longer: the tiredness and the snappy, irritable attitude.
>
> After a period of not flying on this plane she has started to return to her normal bubbly personality. Her confidence is returning and we are so relieved to see that she is more like her old self.

Six fume events aboard the same Boeing 767, from 28 December 2009 to 25 April 2010

Sixteen US Airways pilots and flight attendants in April sued a contractor, ST Aerospace Mobile, over what they claimed was inadequate maintenance, resulting in six fume events aboard the same Boeing 767.[5] The plaintiffs testified to significant symptoms following the six events, as documented in court records:

28 December 2009 – Four plaintiffs reported being exposed to fumes in the passenger compartment, and described symptoms that included headache, sore throat, dizziness, fatigue, skin irritation, stomach pain, eye irritation, difficulty breathing and nausea.

30 December 2009 – Two plaintiffs testified to being affected by a fume event, reporting the following symptoms: headache, difficulty breathing, dizziness, nausea, vomiting, eye irritation, cognitive impairment.

8 January 2010 – One plaintiff reported being exposed to toxic fumes, and described the following acute symptoms: headache, dizziness, fatigue, burning of nose and throat, inability to focus the eyes.

16 January 2010 – Six plaintiffs, including the captain, David Hill, reported ill-health resulting from toxic fumes in the cockpit and passenger compartment. Symptoms included headache, eye irritation, fatigue, cognitive difficulties, irritated throat, neck pain, difficulty breathing and swallowing.

16 March 2010 – Two plaintiffs, including the captain, Thomas Walden, reported exposure to fumes and symptoms that included the following: skin irritation, eye irritation, difficulty breathing, headaches, sore throat, coughing.

25 April 2010 – One plaintiff reported being exposed to toxic fumes, with the following acute symptoms: headache, irritation of eyes, fatigue and cognitive difficulties.

15

Captain's discretion

Once an employee has set a collision course with management, it is very hard to get off it. It is even harder when management are pressing their employees to the limit all the time, and harder still when an employee's hidden ill-heath exacerbates the situation.

I struggled through 2003, flying by rote and instinct, battling against extreme tiredness, disorientation and my mysterious neurological symptoms – which by now I had learned to live with, almost like an actor taking on a new part. I had fifteen years to go before I reached retirement age, and I knew without a shadow of doubt that I could not last that long.

Throughout 2004 the tension with Flybe management was steadily intensifying. It seemed to me that the company was so focused on the principles of accountancy and task management that in seeking to squeeze the last few extra flying hours out of its crews, it was treating them as they were interchangeable robots.

When relations with managers are poor, and you are exhausted yourself, no sane person looks to pick a battle over health and safety issues. I should stress I was not fighting to have aerotoxic syndrome recognized at that time, because I wasn't yet aware of it. Ground managers continued to insist on that bit extra, for that bit less, even if it meant going beyond the bounds of sensible limits or on occasion beyond what was permitted under the law.

Here's one example. On my wife Nicki's birthday, 19 March 2004, I had requested an early duty and early finish so that we could go out for a meal to celebrate as a family. Of course, I had accepted throughout my career that commercial flying has its antisocial elements, and I was well aware that unforeseen circumstances can dash the best-laid plans, but this was an important celebration to me.

There was a lot of tension between ground and air-based

employees at that time, because it is so much more difficult for air-based staff than it is for those with office jobs to schedule their time off or to alter their work commitments to deal with family emergencies. Pressure on scheduling and the relentless emphasis on 'efficiency' had made the issue much more acute. At that time I was working three out of four weekends a month, and with a working wife and children at school I found it hard to fit in with my family's needs and expectations, so I really wanted to keep my promise to Nicki on her birthday.

As a crew we did indeed get an early start, but just before going home we were asked by management to add a further two flights to our basic four-flight schedule. Flybe air crew based at Birmingham (of whom I was one) were normally used as cover crew to fill gaps in the system and help get aircraft where the company wanted them. So we were told to ferry a good BAe 146 to Gatwick, then fly a BAe 146 on three engines (that is, with one of its four engines out of action) to Birmingham for maintenance.

Flying on three engines is legal, but I had only practised a three-engine ferry in the flight simulator. Of course it is more risky than flying a fully serviceable aircraft, especially if there is bad weather or one of the other engines fails. We were already tired, and we would have had to land back in Birmingham in the dark. What was more, it was sure to take us over the statutory maximum hours of flying for the shift. Airlines operate a practice called 'captain's discretion' in which the captain is allowed to sanction two further hours of flying on top of the statutory period, provided that in their judgement, both pilots and cabin crew are fit and able to do the work safely. It should be noted that there is no such discretion in, for example, lorry driving, where the statutory maximum is firmly applied. But these flights would have taken us not just up to, but beyond the limit of the discretionary time, so they were in the realms of illegality.

In practice, 'captain's discretion' is generally perceived to have been replaced by 'ground staff's orders' – and not always senior ground staff, at that. Pilot judgement is regularly overturned by commercial considerations. For example, following the 'red alert' incident at Birmingham that I mentioned earlier I was astounded to be told by our ground operations that I should immediately collect my shaken crew, move to another aircraft, and resume the flight to Jersey. I hadn't even had time to do the Air Safety Report paperwork required by standard operating procedures, and I flatly refused.

So here we were again, being pushed by Ops to go way beyond the extra mile. I had been awake since 4.30 am. Even if I hadn't been keen to get home, neither I nor my crew were in any condition to carry out two further flights, particularly when the last leg would be a risky one. And this was not an emergency situation, it was something we were being told to do for the company's convenience. My first officer, George 'Lima', a former RAF wing commander, agreed with my judgement that we should refuse to do the flights.

The operations director was furious, and didn't hide it. I was shocked that my professional judgement as captain should have been questioned so unpleasantly. Up until then I had always been a loyal employee, but this seriously shook my confidence in our management. After the episode I wrote a letter to senior managers, expressing my concern, not just about this incident, but about the general direction of the company and many of the decisions taken on flying hours and schedules. At first I received no reply at all. Only after I had sent several reminders did the company offer a rather bland and evasive reply, some four months later.

This was in August 2004 – the same month when, as you'll recall from Chapter 1, I left my aircraft – and the airport – and refused to fly to Salzburg because of a combination of factors that, put together, rendered it unsafe for me to fly, in my judgement. The Salzburg incident was another example of the great reluctance of airlines to cancel flights even in the most difficult circumstances. Rather than cancel the flight, the company recalled a pilot who had flown into the airport earlier, and was then on his way home. He agreed to be first officer for the flight that I had thought too risky for me to operate.

I was quite aware that I would be on management's radar for having walked off the BAe 146, and that was all the more true, of course, when someone else successfully completed the assignment I had refused. I knew it would affect my career. Yet as I drove home, with the window down and a fresh breeze in my face, I felt good about my 'Swiss cheese' decision. I hadn't taken an easy way out, I had done what I knew was right.

Schedules and judgements

To begin with, after the Salzburg incident the company seemed uncertain whether to treat my case as disciplinary or medical. Perhaps you have to know the airline industry from the inside to understand this. There's a very strong ethos that you 'get the mission done' regardless of the difficulties. To some extent this derives from the RAF mentality, but commercial flying is a different proposition from military flying. In battle, pilots have to take risks that would not, and should not, be acceptable in the very different civil environment.

I contacted my manager and explained why I had left the flight, but it was clear he was not impressed, so I was not surprised when I was asked to attend what I knew was in effect a disciplinary hearing. The letter I received afterwards is a good example of the ethos I have been discussing. In part it read:

> in future, you complete your duties and then present a formal grievance so that the matter can be properly investigated and, if substantiated, be dealt with. To simply make a stand as you did does not help. It promotes further roster disruption to your colleagues and does little to help with morale. This Company looks to its captains for leadership and to present them as role models to the rest of the work force.

It is worth considering what this implies, because there is an element of both tragedy and farce to it. I'd made the point strongly that my decision not to fly had been based on serious safety concerns. So what the company was effectively telling me was that if I did have safety concerns about a flight, I should ignore them and get on with it, then – if we all survived – make a formal complaint afterwards. I can't imagine that many passengers would be reassured to know their captain had decided it was not safe to fly, but was required to do so anyway, for the sake of company morale.

I found myself grounded – stood down from flying duties. This continued for the rest of 2004 and a short way into 2005. It was a massive shock, and during this period I talked with a number of people to get their opinions about both my own actions and the company's reaction to them. I gained some understanding, including support from my aviation medical examiner (AME), whose report stated that the company was pushing the limits in terms of their operational expectations of pilots, and that it ought to acknowledge this and begin to make adjustments. The issue of chemical poisoning did not come up, because I had not realized that this might be at the root of my problems. I didn't suggest it, and the doctors I saw did not see it as a likely explanation. So the issue here was whether I had been put under too much stress, and this had affected my behaviour. The response was a classic example of the reaction of airlines when they receive criticism of this kind. I learned later that the operations director had written to my AME and complained that I had somehow 'conned' him into showing sympathy.

An ex TNT pilot colleague of mine, Bob Millichap, recommended that I see Professor Gordon Turnbull, a psychiatric adviser to the CAA. He is an eminent psychiatrist, who had helped the former Beirut hostages Terry Waite and John McCarthy. I found this most interesting, since he described to me how the brain works, with the help of diagrams and descriptions of the left side and the right side. I tried to link what I was hearing to the symptoms I was suffering, and the situation I had found myself in, but I must confess that Professor Turnbull was shooting in the dark to some extent, because I did not come clean even to him about the long duration and seriousness of my health problems. He is an acknowledged expert in post-traumatic stress disorder (PTSD), and it is perhaps not surprising that his tentative diagnosis was of this condition: not just because that was what he was looking for, but because it was not unreasonable in the light of what he knew about me. Personally I was surprised. I didn't think that my problems stemmed from trauma, or indeed that I had suffered trauma comparable with that often experienced by members of the emergency services or armed forces. But I can testify at first hand as to how helpful it was to be taken seriously and to be offered a medical label, even if it turned out not to be a correct one.

Professor Turnbull wrote a very supportive letter recommending changes to the operational issues that he felt (rightly) had put me under stress. He even advised that I could return to flying, reinstating my Class 1 aviation medical. However I was reluctant to do this, not just because the airline had not actually changed its operations in light of these recommendations, but also because I continued to feel extremely ill. I also wanted the CAA to investigate the circumstances of the 29 August incident (when I had left the Salzburg flight). Flybe, my employers, did not agree to present the events of that day as an official mandatory occurrence report (MOR), but I had the option to present a report directly to the CAA, as any pilot may do in theory. In practice this does not often happen, not least because airlines are understandably not happy for their staff to submit reports of incidents when their managers consider it unwarranted. It was sure to make me even more unpopular. Even so I went ahead, and the CAA received the MOR in November 2004.

The events that followed this still strike me as deeply unsatisfactory. The CAA was obliged to investigate the matter, and as part of their investigation they considered Flybe's evidence, provided as a closure report. Although I had filed the MOR myself, so I was clearly an interested party, the CAA refused to let me see Flybe's submission. In 2008 I made a request for it to be disclosed under the UK Freedom of Information Act, arguing that it could contain information relating to contaminated air, a safety issue, and that there was therefore a public interest in disclosure. (Although I had not been aware at the time of the incident that contaminated air might have played a part, by this time I was fully aware of the problems it could cause.)

In response the CAA invoked Section 23 of the Civil Aviation Act 1982, which permits it to claim exemption from Freedom of Information requirements. I appealed to the information commissioner. The tribunal panel that heard the appeal was allowed to see the closure report, but again I was not. So plenty of people were permitted to read the official report into this safety-related incident, but the pilot involved was not allowed to see what claims Flybe had made, even though he had asked for the investigation. The tribunal ruling (which went against me) declared that the report did not refer to contaminated air. I have still not been permitted to see it, so have no basis on which to comment on or rebut the evidence that Flybe submitted.

Another concern of mine was that I felt conditions were being tolerated in airlines which would not have been accepted in other fields of work. My wife worked in health and safety and quality management, so I was aware of the standards that are applied elsewhere. At one point I called the Health and Safety Executive for advice. This achieved nothing – they referred me back to the CAA. (This was no wonder, as the UK Health and Safety Executive (HSE) and the CAA had agreed on a Memorandum of Understanding,[1] where the HSE, despite being the primary health and safety regulator, deferred on virtually all aviation safety matters to the CAA.)

It will be useful here to look at two strongly related issues: why aircrew like me with admitted physical problems continue to pass their medical checks, and why 'fume events' are often not reported.

16

Passing the medicals

One thing that may be surprising to readers who are not involved directly in the airline industry is that although I have testified to years of serious health problems, I had no real difficulty in passing the regular medicals that pilots are subjected to. Does this mean that I wasn't as ill as I'm making out? Or does it mean that these checks are not as effective a safety precaution as they are supposed to be?

I can assure you that I have not exaggerated my symptoms, and at times it surprised me that I actually did pass the medical checks I was given. Let us look at why this happens.

The requirements for individuals to qualify as commercial pilots are very stringent: they need to have good academic qualifications, be in good health, and have clocked up plenty of flying experience. Qualifying as cabin crew is not quite as demanding, but cabin crew too have to meet a number of conditions, including (in the United Kingdom, and in many other countries) passing a medical examination. All pilots have to take a repeat medical examination at least every six or twelve months depending on their age.

But while many professions and occupations have stringent requirements for those joining them, which do indeed exclude less fit individuals, once people have qualified the emphasis changes, and the general presumption is that people will keep their professional status. It's not in anyone's interest for aircrew to fail their checks. It's a disaster for the individual if that happens, and it creates difficulty for their employer too. So, just as individuals put a lot of effort into making sure they pass their tests, the examiners too are predisposed to letting people pass, because they know how traumatic it is to fail someone.

Aircrew also play their part in planning their careers so as to minimize any risk of failure. I mentioned in Chapter 13 how I made the decision not to try to move from the BAe 146 I knew so well to a different type of aircraft because the conversion training would have been too challenging. I'm sure many other pilots have made the same kinds of decision, to avoid being put in situations that could expose the physical and neurological problems they are experiencing.

There were several occasions when even so, I felt I was lucky not to have been found out.

Everyone knows where they were, and what they were doing, on 11 September 2001. I remember it particularly well because I was on a training course that week in Southampton, studying to become an airline training captain – that is, someone qualified to train other pilots. I was feeling more than usually ill, as I had felt since 1990. I was filmed giving a 45-minute presentation to my colleagues, and I cringe with embarrassment now when I watch the recording. I sounded as if I was drunk, and had scrambled and mispronounced many of my words. I apologized afterwards to colleagues, but if they noticed, they chose to overlook the problems. I also noticed that I had used many 'non-words' in my presentation. I would not have given myself a pass, but to my surprise, I was passed as a training captain. I hid the VHS tape of the presentation until 2007, when I realized it provided important evidence of my physical speech problems.

In a slightly different context, my difficulties became all too apparent in October 2003, when I was invited to fly a simple motor glider by a good friend Mike 'Charlie', a fellow Flybe captain. It sounded like a great opportunity. I had always loved the feeling of independence and freedom that goes with flying small aircraft, a situation in which pilots don't have to worry about pressure from management and all the other hassles that can make modern commercial flying much less of a pleasure.

Mike arranged for us to fly a two-seat motor glider from Enstone, an airfield in north Oxfordshire. The plan was for him to start off, to introduce me to the little aircraft. Then after about an hour, we reckoned I should be sufficiently acquainted with the routine to handle her on my own.

That was the theory. But as soon as we were airborne I realized to my horror that I was not coping. I struggled to follow Mike's instructions. The controls were much simpler than those of a passenger airliner, but I still couldn't retain all the information I needed to handle them. In aviation jargon, I was 'behind' this slow aircraft.

Mike and I completed some circuits around the airfield. Even though I wasn't feeling happy about the situation, I took the controls for the descent and landing. After all, the point of the trip had been for me to fly, not just to sit by Mike, and I didn't feel I could admit I wasn't confident to do it. But I was right not to be confident, because as we landed I must have over-corrected a small error and we hit the runway with a crash. The little plane slithered to an ungainly halt. Fortunately the damage of a broken seat was only minor, but it was acutely embarrassing to make the sort of error a rookie would make in front of a professional colleague. I vividly recall Mike attempting to shrug it off. That was kind of him, but in retrospect perhaps he should not have been so generous. This was another occasion when someone might have alerted the airline to my condition, but (from the very best of motives) chose not to do so.

Let me make a confession here: as well as experiencing leniency from those assessing me, I have been an assessor myself – and been lenient myself. Here is a good example.

On Wednesday 25 August 2004 I was rostered to complete a line check on a Birmingham-based flight crew. I was a training captain at the time, and my job was to check that the crew were following standard operating procedures (SOPs) correctly. So I joined them for a relatively short flight from Birmingham to Belfast City and back, on which I had to observe the crew's routines and ensure they did everything correctly.

The pilot and the other crew members were very experienced, and this was a familiar route for them, so I was expecting to be able to tick all the boxes and rate the performance as 'Good'. But things got off to a bad start when the captain of the flight (who was also one of my fellow training captains) launched into a rant about Flybe's chaotic rostering system. Not only was he unhappy about the way the company was treating him, his crew were an unhappy bunch too. The changes that had been made to the rosters meant they had to do these flights when they were already fatigued. And they made mistakes.

I was in the middle seat of the cockpit as the check pilot, so I couldn't fail to notice that what should have been a normal ILS (instrument landing system) approach to Belfast City didn't go according to plan, simply because the crew failed to follow SOPs. They allowed the aircraft to fly at a greater speed than normal through the extended centreline of Belfast

City's runway, then they had to scramble to get onto the glide path to descend. The pilots then chatted throughout the muddled approach about 'jumbo jets in cross-wind landings' in an apparent attempt to try to distract me from what I had witnessed. Not only did it fail to distract me, it worried me more. Another SOP is that there should be a 'sterile cockpit' when the aircraft is flying below 10,000 feet; in other words that the crew should only talk about matters directly relevant to the flight during takeoff and landing. This conversation wasn't relevant at all, so in itself it was breaking the SOP.

Then when we were getting ready to leave Belfast and head back to Birmingham, the captain – who was now the non-flying pilot, since his first officer took over for the return flight – was required to read through a 'Before start' checklist. The trouble was, he clipped the 'After landing' checklist in front of him on the control column. He didn't notice, because he knew the checklist by heart, and there was nothing wrong with his memory, but that wasn't an excuse. The SOP is that the person running through the checks must use the checklist, and it's not acceptable to work from recall. At this point, I was forced to intervene and point out his mistake. After all, I was a passenger as well as being a tester, and it was important for everyone on board that the checklist, an essential part of the safety system, be followed properly.

Remember, this wasn't a standard flight, this was one where the crew knew they were being checked on, so it wasn't a case of their cutting corners when nobody was watching. And they were making the kinds of mistake which would have meant failure, were this instead the test for a trainee pilot. But I hesitated over what to do about the situation. I believed this was a fundamentally safe crew who were simply exhausted, victims of the punishing rostering system. What was more, they were friends, so the last thing I wanted to do was to punish them for their fatigue.

But could I actually pass them when they had made so many basic errors? I could have asked them to redo the line check, going to Shannon and back, but when I was sure the main problem was their tiredness, it would have been perverse to make them even more exhausted. After some thought, I came to a compromise. I quizzed them on why they had made so many errors, including some basic ones, and graded them 'Average' rather than the usual 'Good'. I also called the head trainer afterwards to describe what had happened. Far from criticizing me for bending the system, he thanked me for making a sensible decision. I also recommended that examiners should be from a different base from the crew being tested, because it compromises the objectivity that is supposed to be built into the system if people are assessing their friends. I understand this proposal was considered but rejected because it would have meant additional travel and accommodation costs for crews and examiners.

17

To report or not to report

One thing we have already seen in this book – and will see more when we look in detail at research into fume events and the response to it – is that there's a big gap between what many aircrew perceive as a common problem, and many airlines, regulators and politicians perceive as something rare. The explanation is simple. As we have also seen, the vast majority of fume events go unreported.

There are quite a few reasons for this, and they are worth spelling out.

- First, there's no easy way to define a 'fume event' or 'smoke incident', because in real life these incidents can fall anywhere on a spectrum of seriousness which includes, at one end, releases of toxic materials that don't produce either smoke or a bad smell, and can go entirely unnoticed, and at the other end, dramatic incidents such as the one when I experienced a 'fire in the toilet' on a BAe 146 which actually turned out to be an unambiguously visible fume event. Of course that latter event got formally reported but the vast majority of the more 'routine' events don't. It has been estimated from BALPA research that only 3.66 per cent of all fume events are actually reported.[1]
- You might think it would be possible to define a clear cut-off point. If cabin air was being monitored in real time, then it would be apparent when dangerous substances got into it. Does that happen? The answer is no – there are no air quality measuring devices fitted to commercial airliners, despite repeated recommendations by various bodies. Should it happen? Absolutely, and the 1964 (US) FAR Ventilation Regulation spells this out: 'There must be provisions to ensure that [the] crew and passenger compartment air must be free from harmful ... gasses or vapors.'[2]
- Next, airlines don't like to make reports of events that

jeopardize passenger and crew safety. No one likes emergencies. If one is declared, lots of trouble and cost follows. The flight might have to be cancelled, or the aircraft grounded until it has been checked out and cleared for further service. Investigations by aviation authorities are expensive and time-consuming, for both the authority and the airline whose incident is being investigated. If there's a crash or an emergency landing, there's no question – a report *will* be made and an investigation follow. But a bit of a smell in the cabin, a few passengers complaining of smarting eyes? It's much easier to overlook that and decide it doesn't warrant a report.

- Not only do airline management not like reports, aircrew don't like them either. They entail a lot of extra work. Hard-pressed aircrew really don't *want* to have to fill in lengthy, complicated forms, and respond to questions from investigators afterwards. It's a hassle they could do without. When you are routinely flying four flights a day, with tight turnarounds, there is little time to reflect on past events. An air safety report has many sections, and all manner of details are compulsory, including some that are often not relevant to the type of incident, such as local air temperature. We all hate what we perceive is a waste of time, checking out and completing details such as this.
- Crews are all too aware that no one earns merit points by reporting safety issues. Like whistleblowers in every field, there might be encouragement and protection in theory, but in practice those who make complaints get labelled as troublemakers, and are often made to suffer for it.
- Expectations change over time. Aircrew moving to work on an aircraft that's notorious for its smoke incidents, like the BAe 146, might be concerned at first when those noxious fumes spread through the cabin during the start-up routine. After a few dozen, or a few hundred, occurrences, they get to take it for granted. By this stage many of them don't even ask themselves if they ought to fill in a safety report. They assume that the situation has been checked out, and there's nothing new that anyone needs to be told about.
- In some cases, reports on investigations into accidents or other incidents do not appear until many years later. The

long delays until you hear anything back tend to reduce motivation to engage in the reporting process.

- And finally, those who are in poor health find it particularly hard to summon up the energy to pursue this kind of issue. Karen Isherwood, whose 'holiday to Hell' experience I describe in Chapter 36, had plenty to grumble about, but she never actually put in a formal complaint to Ryanair. She did contact the airline, but as she put it, 'they said to put it in writing which I never did as I have been consumed with trying to feel better and getting my life on track'. I felt much the same myself in early 2003, after the 'red alert' incident. Neither I nor the rest of my crew had the time or the energy to pursue the issue of the anomalies between the company's version of our events and what we felt had happened.

So it's dangerous to assume that because an event hasn't been reported, there *was* no event. However, that is all too often what seems to happen, as we shall learn.

18

Problem? What problem?

When campaigners have been working literally for decades to spread the word about the dangers of fumes on aircraft, and when we believe there is a mountain of evidence, it's not just frustrating, it is infuriating to find that there's still official denial. But to a large extent, that's the case.

We'll look at some of the reasons why this is so shortly. But let me report now on a debate in the UK House of Lords on 18 March 2014, as I was finalizing this book.[1] Similar examples could be probably found in any developed country. It is an alarming indication of how far we still have to go to put our case across. Baroness Kramer was at this time a minister of state for transport – not the lead minister, but a member of the ministerial team – in the UK coalition government. She is responding to questions put by other members of the House of Lords, the UK's upper house of Parliament.

The Countess of Mar (Crossbench)

My Lords, it is almost sixty years since the danger of fumes seeping into cabin air was first reported. With the notable exception of the Boeing 787, virtually all passenger jets still have flawed and potentially dangerous bleed air systems, a design that leaks pyrolised oil into the air supply. Does the Minister agree that most shocking of all is the fact that airlines fail to inform passengers that they have been exposed, which – and I have chosen my words very carefully – must be a breach of passengers' rights and casts a dark reflection on the aviation industry? What solutions does the Minister have?

Baroness Kramer (Liberal Democrat)

My Lords, on most commercial aircraft the cabin air supply is provided by engine bleed air, which is drawn from the compressor stage of the engine. Contamination, known as a fume event, may occur when oil or hydraulic fluid is released into the bleed air – for example, as a result of an oil seal failure – resulting in the formation of a fleeting odour or mist in the aircraft cabin. Most fume events last less than a minute or two.

Many investigations have been carried out by the department, of which the noble Countess will be well aware. The Committee on Toxicity concluded that there was no evidence for pollutants occurring in cabin at levels exceeding available health and safety standards and guidelines and, as most levels observed were comparable to those typically experienced in domestic settings, there is appropriately no requirement for passengers to be informed. There are many steps to be taken if there is an assessment that there is any endangerment to any passengers or to the flight.

Lord Tyler (Liberal Democrat)

My Lords, is my noble friend aware of the work undertaken by the all-party parliamentary organophosphate group, of which the noble Countess and I were both members? Can she in particular tell us whether there is continuous monitoring of incidents and potential risks, following the Cranfield study some years ago? It is my impression that there is no continuing monitoring – I do not think that there has been any recent report on this – of incidence in a global sense, even if there is one for UK operators.

Baroness Kramer (Liberal Democrat)

My Lords, as your Lordships will be aware, for six years the department carried out significant research into these issues, and quite appropriately so. That research led to four studies, the main one of which was the Cranfield study published in May 2011. All four reports were sent to the Committee on Toxicity, which also peer-reviewed other international data and came to the conclusion that I just discussed: that cabin air at levels exceeding available health and safety standards and guidelines was not evident in any of those studies. Going forward, I think it therefore becomes an international issue and it is a matter for the European Aviation Safety Agency or the International

Civil Aviation Organisation to consider whether more research should be done. At this point, I am not aware of any concerns that they have for ongoing monitoring or further research.

So what the UK government thinks is that there is no health and safety issue; there is no evidence; there is no reason for any further investigation or research.

I and my colleagues are convinced there are medical effects as a consequence to exposure to contaminated air (containing organophosphates) and described as 'aerotoxic syndrome' on aircraft.

19

The end of a career

When did my career as a pilot end and my new career as a campaigner begin? Before I tell you about that, let me continue the story of my time at Flybe – and its unhappy ending.

The summary air incident report on the Salzburg flight that I had refused to fly – written by the company, not the CAA, which had chosen not to carry out its own independent investigation – landed on my doorstep in April 2005. It horrified me.

It is a long-standing convention in air incident reports that the staff involved remain anonymous. The report is not a disciplinary hearing. Its main purpose is to identify, in as objective a way as possible, any weaknesses in systems, so that these can be corrected. If the investigators judge that employees deserve criticism, this is something that is handled separately. So I was appalled to see my name appear several times in the summary report. Worse, there were serious factual errors about the events of that day. I felt these errors tended to place me in an unjustifiably bad light, and I even contemplated libel action.

This I did not pursue, but I did contact my union (BALPA), and with their help, lodged a formal grievance. When I wasn't happy with the way this procedure was handled I lodged an appeal, and these processes continued up to June 2005 – the month of my last flight with Flybe, and as it would turn out, my last ever flight as an airline pilot.

That last flight happened on 30 June, a fine summer's day when I and my colleagues were scheduled to make four flights: a regular short-hop return between Birmingham and Edinburgh, then another between Birmingham and Brest in western France. Our aircraft was a BAe 146, one of the oldest in the fleet and in increasing need of maintenance.

I decided to do the first flight, with my first officer Nick 'Lima' doing 'pilot not flying' (PNF) duties – radio and monitoring. We would then swap around for the subsequent flights. About five minutes before we were to land in Edinburgh, the rear cabin crew reported to us that there were fumes and a bad smell at the back of the cabin. There was no fire as far as we knew, and no reason for emergency measures, so we landed as normal and parked the aircraft.

When I went to the back of the aircraft I saw what the crew had meant; there was a nasty acidic, almost electrical smell. Then I was told there *was* a fire after all, in the rear luggage hold, and so I dashed outside to investigate. This proved to be a false alarm, but the baggage handlers were understandably complaining about the fumes.

We were 'tech', to use aviation jargon – that is, we had technical problems which would inevitably hold up any further flights in the aircraft. The dispatcher then came on board to ask when we wanted our next passengers. Every pilot gets accustomed to this sometimes unsubtle pressure to keep the show on the road. I thought it might take some time to find and fix the problem, and suggested it might be a good idea to source another crew and aircraft for the Brest flights. There was a risk that if this was not done, our crew could run well over the legal maximum number of duty hours.

The maintenance engineer eventually identified a burnt-out electrical motor under the floor near the back of the aircraft. In total, we were on the ground for 3 hours and 28 minutes – the usual turnaround time being 35 minutes. The return flight was mostly straightforward – no more of the unpleasant smells – but on our descent the warning light for undercarriage came on at 1,500 feet. We had forgotten to put the wheels down! Fortunately the alerting system warned us in time and we had a safe landing, but it was a worrying (and uncharacteristic) error for two such experienced pilots. The hassle of the delay had made us even more tired than usual.

After shutting the aircraft down I telephoned operations to confirm that we would not be doing the flight to Brest. We couldn't have done it without exceeding our legal hours, so it seemed an entirely uncontroversial decision. But it didn't go down well, as it turned out that there was no reserve crew to do the Brest flights. Before long, I was being interviewed over the phone by a manager (a stranger to me) asking me for more information on our 'refusal' to fly to Brest. I was told that for the crew to 'take the next two flights off' we had to be registered as 'sick'. I felt that this was absurd, but at least this was a way to end the debate over whether we should fly, so we all agreed to being defined as 'sick', and were stood down and despatched to the airfield doctor. As we had been exposed to the fumes on the outbound flight, perhaps this was no bad thing.

A few days later – on a day off – the Flybe flight safety officer phoned me. He told me that as the outward flight on 30 June had been affected by a fume event, we should not have flown back to Birmingham. It had been illegal to do so, he said. When the airline had pressed us so hard not only to make this flight, but to make two more afterwards – and had not shown any concern for their legality at the time – this struck me as blatant hypocrisy. It confirmed to me what I had already sensed, that it was time to bring my career at Flybe to an end.

I spent the remainder of my time as a Flybe employee on sick leave. I still felt seriously ill, still with very pervasive symptoms, yet every doctor I saw diagnosed me as suffering from stress, depression, chronic fatigue and similar nebulous mental problems. Naturally I was affected by depression, at times quite intense, but only as a by-product of my physical symptoms and their effect on my career and family life. In December 2005 I asked my GP for help, and he prescribed me anti-depressants. When I read about the side-effects I decided not to take them, as I have always tried to avoid any unnecessary drugs. I reckon in retrospect that this was a wise decision. When you are sick with chemical poisoning, taking drugs won't make you better, and can make you much, much worse. I also saw Professor Turnbull (see page 67) again, in late 2005. During the consultation, I recall that my speech was particularly jumbled, and I probably sounded rather manic. All he had to offer (apart from sympathy) was Prozac, which I again declined.

By this time I was desperate to make a reasonably dignified exit from Flybe, to bring this miserable phase to an end, and I hoped to begin to rebuild my shattered life. I was recommended by BALPA to negotiate a retirement on sickness grounds. This would pave the way for me to receive a 'loss of licence' payment.

I needed medical certification as part of this process, and was offered a choice of two assessors, Captain Julian Soddy of BALPA, or Professor Michael Bagshaw, an experienced doctor who specialized in health problems related to aviation, and was an adviser to the CAA. I elected to go with Professor Bagshaw as a medical doctor, and he interviewed me in early 2006.

Our interview took place at the Flybe headquarters in Exeter, Devon. Professor Bagshaw was on first-name terms with my Flybe fleet manager, which struck me as odd, and strikes me now as rather worrying. I'm not suggesting that Professor Bagshaw has behaved unethically, but it is certainly true that although as we shall learn, there had already been a considerable amount of research into fume incidents and aerotoxic syndrome, the suggestion that this might be at the root of my health problems was never raised in my interview with this acknowledged expert in aviation health.

I told Professor Bagshaw that my 'bucket was full' and that I couldn't face the stresses of airline flying again. He agreed that I was in a bad way, and put in his report that 'I wasn't prepared to go the final mile' and that I should be allowed to retire as a result of 'chronic stress'. I didn't agree with some of the points he made, but his report did indeed lead to my being retired on health grounds and securing a loss of licence payment. It was only later that I really came to regret the fact that I had joined many others in dismissing the evidence of the real major cause of my problems.

20

Evidence? What evidence?

I mentioned in Chapter 8 one of aviation journalist Andy Weir's examples of potential 'tombstone' events involving toxic fumes. This one occurred on 12 November 1999 near Malmo, Sweden. It's worth looking at what happened, because the potential for disaster was so clear on this flight.

This incident occurred on a short internal flight between Stockholm and Malmo in a BAe 146. As the aircraft was approaching its destination, Malmo/Sturup airport, the co-pilot suddenly felt nauseous. He reached for and put on his oxygen mask. About ten seconds later, the commander, Neils Gomer, also became very nauseous, and he too reached for his oxygen mask. The co-pilot felt better within a few seconds of switching to breathing oxygen, but the captain continued to feel 'dizzy and groggy' (in the words of the report on the incident) for some time. He had difficulty with physiological motor response, multi-tasking and in focusing, and handed over the controls to the co-pilot. During the approach, the purser went into the cabin to tell the pilots the cabin was prepared for landing, and as well as seeing that both pilots were using their masks, she noticed that the captain seemed to have difficulty grasping her finger, the gesture he usually made to acknowledge what she had told him when using a full face oxygen mask.

The pilots landed the aircraft successfully. The crew noticed that several of the passengers who disembarked – several of whom they knew, since the passengers and crew both flew that route regularly – 'seemed passive and more tired than normal'. The report also noted that 'After the incident, the commander was shaking and in a cold sweat.'[1] He slept deeply and continued to experience symptoms for 24 hours.

Post-flight maintenance checks soon found the cause: there was an external oil leak on engine number 2, which had caused oil fumes to seep into the cabin. Captain Gomer later said in an interview for a BBC *Panorama* documentary, 'One of the engineers showed me. Where the engine was supposed to be totally clean of oil, where the bleed air is taken to go into the cabin and cockpit for us to breathe, it was just dripping with oil.'[2]

If the pilots had been any slower to react, they might well have been unable to recover and land the jet. They acknowledge that they only managed to fit their oxygen masks just in time. Did this ensure that the problem of fume events was taken seriously? No, not really. Perhaps it requires the potential corpses to become actual corpses in a clear and unmistakeable major incident before anything serious is done to bring the problem to an end.

We have seen that even today, many people – not just airline staff, but safety experts, regulatory authorities and politicians – refuse to acknowledge that there is a problem called aerotoxic syndrome. Now it is time to look at some of the evidence that actually has accumulated, and to examine some of the reasons why research has not yet properly addressed the attitude that contaminated air problems are all in the sufferers' minds.

One of the first countries to take the problem seriously was Australia. In the period 1999–2001 it held a major parliamentary inquiry into the health of pilots and crew. This looked at jet aircraft generally, but with a particular focus on the BAe 146, following up on reports of ill health and concerns over cabin air quality. It concluded that the aircraft were in breach of existing airworthiness regulations, and that there was a clear link between poor quality cabin air and health problems among flight crew. (I am not sure why the report focused so narrowly on aircrew. For every affected pilot there must be at least three cabin crew and hundreds of affected passengers, from holidaymakers to heads of state.)

The report made a raft of recommendations, particularly on monitoring cabin air quality and better maintenance, few of which were implemented. Nearly a decade later the chair of the inquiry, the Reverend John Woodley, by then retired from the Australian Senate, said that the report would have been even more damning had British Aerospace and Ansett Airlines not withheld some information. If he had had all the relevant information, he would have 'recommended that the BAe 146 aircraft fleet be grounded until a solution could be found to safeguard the health and flight safety of the travelling public and aircrew'.[3]

So behind the scenes the aviation industry was well aware of the problem, but it was certainly not eager to let the details emerge. This research didn't cross my radar at the time, and I wasn't alone in this. Very few people in the industry were aware of the rising concerns. It was only later that, for example, David Learmount, safety editor of the aviation sector journal *Flight International,* began to cover this emerging issue in some depth.

At this time there was movement too in the United States. In mid-2001 the US National Research Council was on the brink of publishing a damning critique of the aviation industry's limited response to a 1986 report (yes, that's 1986: almost thirty years ago) on the quality of cabin air.[4] The only substantial measure it recommended which was implemented was a ban on cigarette smoking in aircraft. It also recommended continuous monitoring of air quality on flights, and a programme to monitor the health of aircrew. It clearly established that oil seal breaches can on occasion lead to oil leaking into the compressor and forming a vapour in the cabin.

Note the date, though: mid-2001. 9/11 threw everything back into play. Security leapt to the top of the agenda, and the notorious British civil servant who sent colleagues a message 'This is a good day to bury bad news' was not alone. Nobody wanted to hear about cabin air issues in this environment, and the NRC's report was one of the pieces of bad news that was buried in the stampede to focus on precautions against terrorists.

A follow-up report was published in January 2002, entitled *The Airliner Cabin Environment and the Health of Passengers and Crew*. It concluded that contaminants from engine lubricating oils, hydraulic fluids, de-icing fluids, and by-products of these liquids do leak into cabin air under normal operating conditions. It called for Congress to follow up with funding for further research to determine the toxicity of such chemicals; links with ill-health among flight crews; and the potential for such effects to be exacerbated by the particular features of pressurized cabins, such as low pressure and humidity, and higher levels of ozone than are found in the air at ground level.

In February 2002 the US Federal Aviation Authority (FAA) published a report that welcomed the NRC's findings; but the aviation industry across the world, and in the United States in particular, was busy adjusting to the 9/11 reality, and its recommendations did not really receive the attention that I believe they merited.

The report is freely accessible on the FAA's website at the time of writing, and is well worth reading. One passage reads:

> Viewed as a whole, NRC's report should be seen as evidence that passengers and crewmembers on commercial aircraft have a continuing concern about a variety of health and comfort problems that they ascribe to poor air quality in airliner cabins. Such concerns are not a new phenomenon. NRC conducted a similar study fifteen years ago and presented similar findings and recommendations. Some actions were taken as a result of the 1986 study, notably the ban on smoking on all US domestic flights. However, neither NRC nor FAA has sufficient data to assess objectively passenger and crewmembers' complaints, design effective interventions, or determine whether rulemaking or guidance will be the most effective tactic for making changes.[5]

This is not just disappointing; it is a deeply worrying response to what had been flagged up clearly as a potentially serious health issue. And even after these reports, the implementation of NRC recommendations was uneven. Those that remain largely (and sometimes entirely) unfulfilled include continuous monitoring of the bleed air system, with indicators on the flight deck; aircrew training on the dangers of fumes from engine oil; revised FAA regulations on air quality; and research into air-cleaning technologies and the components of oils and hydraulic fluids.

There were some outcomes, however. In 2003 the US Congress passed legislation (Public Law 108-176, S815) directing the FAA to fund research into cabin air quality. Most of the funding went to the Airliner Cabin Environment Research (ACER) consortium, which together with the Occupational Health Research Consortium in Aviation (OHRCA), received a two-year grant for research into fume events. In those two years, however, the teams were unable to secure the agreement of a single airline to permit flight attendants to carry a portable air sampler on board.

This led the researchers to carry air samplers themselves onto commercial flights. They analysed fifty-five samples, ten of which (18 per cent) tested positive for at least one TCP isomer. It is important to note that these samplings were on flights without visible smoke or a recorded fume event, so they do not reflect the exceptional exposure that individuals receive during these events. They reflect an everyday level of the presence of these highly toxic chemicals.[6]

The researchers also carried out a health survey of flight attendants. A high proportion of them reported that they suffered from neurological and respiratory complaints. Because these were self-reports by the individuals, of problems for which they had not necessarily sought medical attention, it was hard for the researchers to make a definitive link between the complaints and air quality issues on the aircraft. But the researchers recommended that there be further investigation, and I certainly agree. This was one rare occasion when a state-funded study had managed to bypass industry resistance and produce some findings that ought to have caused alarm both across the aviation world and among the general public. But as we have seen, even this did not change the paradigm that there is not a problem that calls for further research.

I described the health problems suffered by Susan Michaelis, an Australian former BAe 146 pilot whom I met at the first Global Cabin Air Quality Executive (GCAQE) meeting in 2006, in Chapter 2. She later completed a PhD on *Health and Flight Safety Implications from Exposure to Contaminated Air in Aircraft*, and her thesis – completed in 2010 – contains a summary and analysis of many of these inquiries.[7] Susan looked particularly for possible evidence of industry lobbying that might have watered down the conclusions and recommendations of the studies. She detected a number of changes between the FAA's final and 'full' report, and the material (described as deriving from this report), that was posted on its website as a response to the NRC. Crucially, the full report contains a damning conclusion that aircraft were in breach of existing airworthiness regulations. This does not feature in the consolidated version on the website.

Flybe itself also commissioned some research. This was not directly focused on aerotoxic syndrome, but it did derive from the company's acknowledgement that it had a problem with pilot turnover. Some pilots had departed for other flying jobs, something that has to be expected by a budget airline when flying the larger long-haul aircraft for major airlines is a more stable and better-paid option. But a further number had been grounded for medical reasons, and Flybe commissioned a psychologist and transport safety academic from Cranfield University, Bedfordshire, Professor Helen Muir, to investigate the underlying causes.

I volunteered to take part in the autumn of 2005, and went to Cranfield to be interviewed by Professor Muir. I showed her my rosters and log book, and talked about how tight schedules and late changes to crewing and scheduling – all of which had become increasingly common – put aircrew under considerable stress. I did not mention aerotoxic syndrome as I was still unaware of it, and neither did she during this interview. I have never seen her report.

21

Real causes, real research

I make no claim to be the discoverer of aerotoxic syndrome. On the contrary, I had not even heard of it until a year after my flying career ended, even though the research I mentioned in Chapter 20 had pointed up a major problem several years earlier, and the incidents that led to that research occurred in 1954.

In 2005 I recall chatting with another Flybe BAe 146 captain from the same crew room at Birmingham. He had transferred to fly the Boeing 737, but had struggled with the training. The reason was simple: he suffered from some of the same symptoms that I had. This shocked me, particularly as I had assumed on meeting him that he was in normal good health and he *looked* so well.

My personal breakthrough came a few months later in early 2006 when I was contacted by Captain Tristan Loraine, a BA Boeing 757 pilot. On behalf of BALPA, he was working on tests for pilots who were union members that were designed to analyse whether they had been affected by contaminated air in airliners. Was I willing to be tested by researchers at University College London? I was intrigued, and very happy to help the union's efforts in the interests of aircrew health, so I agreed. I also put Tristan in touch with two other BAe 146 pilot friends from Flybe. One was a close friend who had told me he had been suffering from severe exhaustion, and wondered about the causes of it. Another was the pilot I mentioned above, who had failed the Boeing 737 course. Unfortunately he was not able to participate in the research because his native tongue was Iranian, and some of the tests were designed for native English speakers. He told me he was confined to home, watching his goldfish swim round and round, and in some personal trouble. In the years to come, I would hear many heartbreaking stories from medically retired pilots, other aircrew and passengers.

The UCL research team was led by Dr Sarah Mackenzie Ross. Tristan had put together twenty-seven current or former pilots, around half of whom had flown BAe 146s and the rest Boeing 757s, another aircraft notorious in the industry for its frequent fume events. It was a self-selecting group which did not pretend to be statistically representative of all pilots, because all the participants had reported being exposed to fumes in cabin air, and all of them had suffered from spells of ill-health. My tests took place in March 2006. At this point I had not been flying for several months, and I felt a little better, but my memory was still poor and my speech still impaired.

I felt there was an air of fear and adventure about the UCL research process. There was a sense that we were engaged in a vaguely subversive enterprise. These were not tests sponsored by aircraft manufacturers or airlines, they were union-supported and funding was tight. Participants were given extensive memory and cognition tests lasting about four hours, and our blood and fat were tested at a private laboratory. The latter two tests were not cheap: they cost around £500 per pilot. I understand Tristan paid for them upfront, though he was later able to claim reimbursement. I was told in 2009 – by the health insurer BUPA, not an airline – that a fat test was painful and inadvisable, and none of the doctors I had consulted had suggested one. This turned out to be completely untrue. It simply involves a jab from a hypodermic syringe in the buttocks, which is no more painful than any injection.

While we were waiting for the results (which took a few weeks) I received a phone call from the university. Was I a cigarette smoker? I had smoked cigars occasionally, but had never been a cigarette smoker, and I was fairly sure this was the case for most, if not all, of the other pilots in the research. The question worried me: were the test results disturbing? It reminded me that on occasion during my career as a pilot, aviation doctors had mentioned 'odd' readings in tests on my kidneys and heart. They never expanded on this comment and further testing showed normal results.

Another thing I recalled was reading a report in *Private Eye* (a satirical and investigative UK magazine) in 2000. The late Paul Foot, well known as a fearless campaigning journalist, had written about toxins in cabin air.[1] At the time I had dismissed it, but now I wondered if these details might prove to be significant pieces in the jigsaw that would help it to evolve into a coherent picture.

Tristan had to battle to get the UCL results into the public domain, just as he had had to battle hard to find a willing academic and get the research completed. It was no wonder, because the findings released in the late spring of 2006 were explosive.[2] Nine pilots (including me probably, as I was particularly ill at the time) were excluded from group analysis of cognitive function because they had a medical or psychiatric history that might otherwise explain their symptoms of ill-health. Of the other eighteen pilots, tests on their language, perceptual and general intellectual ability showed that they were preserved, but their performance on tests of psychomotor speed attention and executive function was below expected levels. 'Indeed, the pilots reported alarming cognitive failures at work, such as being unable to retain numerical information from air traffic control. Nine were still flying, four were on sick leave and five had retired.'

These results were particularly significant because the requirements to qualify as a pilot mean that when they had received their licences, they would all have scored well above the average for the general population. The researchers concluded that there was a flight safety issue because many of the pilots had reported getting confused over numerical data and completing tasks in the correct sequence.

The laboratory analysis supported the evidence from the cognitive tests. Twenty out of the full sample of twenty-seven pilots underwent fat and blood analysis, and all of them were found to have higher than population average levels of one or more volatile organic compounds. Remember, these tests were done on pilots who had suffered from ill-health, so several had already left the profession, as I had by then, and others had not been flying when certified as sick, so the levels would have been lower than if tests had been taken while they were flying the problem planes. My tests had been done about nine months after my final flight, but they still showed a significantly higher than average level of organophosphates in my body fat.

Dr Mackenzie Ross told the BBC *Panorama* programme in 2008:

> My conclusion is that there is definitely something wrong with these pilots. We've been able to exclude common causes for it. The pilots are concerned that it may be exposure to toxic fumes in the aircraft, and certainly the pattern and nature of the difficulties they report is consistent with that seen in other groups of people who have been exposed to chemicals that are potentially toxic to the nervous system.[3]

Not only did I now have a proper sense of the cause of my problems, I also had a name for them. Tristan was the first to tell me in June 2006 that what I had suffered from was known as aerotoxic syndrome.

22

Real media attention

The results of the UCL research not only focused my own mind on the issue of toxins, they focused many other minds too. Tristan Loraine subsequently became a great friend. As well as doing my own investigations, I learned a lot through him, and in many respects he saved my life.

In the autumn of 2006 Tristan invited me to a world first: a conference, hosted in the United Kingdom, to discuss cabin air quality, bravely sponsored by the Independent Pilots Association (IPA). Sarah Mackenzie Ross from UCL was among the other attendees. The body that emerged from the conference became known as the Global Cabin Air Quality Executive (GCAQE) (www.gcaqe.org). It now represents over twenty organizations worldwide, mostly trade unions, but also including the consumer rights group Holiday Travel Watch. Tristan became one of its co-chairs, and the other is Judith Anderson, industrial hygienist with the US-based union the Association of Flight Attendants. The Executive has published research, maintains a website, and holds an annual conference. The organization's description of itself is 'A global coalition of health and safety advocates committed to raising awareness and finding solutions to poor air quality in aircraft'.

At the conference I met dozens of pilots from all over the world, some of them much worse affected than me, coming together to try to advance awareness of the issue. One was an old colleague of mine from TNT, Neils Gomer. He described to me his very serious fume event in which he had narrowly avoided disaster, putting on his oxygen mask just in time to recover his flying faculties (which I outlined in Chapter 20). He too had lost his job as a pilot, and was then driving a bulldozer for a living instead of commanding a BAe 146.

The media were also showing some interest in the issue, which helped greatly. Channel 4 television news made an excellent report with the help of the IPA.[1] It included interviews with pilots who described feeling inebriated after fume events, a feeling that I knew from my own first experience back in 1990. I took part in this as a 'new' sick pilot, though my voice was dubbed and my face was not shown, because I was still technically a Flybe employee (I formally left the company at the end of 2006) and was suing my employers (successfully) for additional compensation at the time. The disguise was far from total, and friends had no problem identifying my hairy arms and blue checked shirt!

But if I had felt that we had achieved unstoppable momentum, I was soon disabused of that idea. My own feeling was that we needed to set up an association to coordinate publicity and research, but when I met up with a group of other affected pilots at Tristan's house in January 2007, I found they had a range of views. Susan Michaelis and Tristan were clearly determined to push on as hard as possible to get official recognition of the problem, but others took a more measured approach. Many of them still had jobs that were on the periphery of the industry, and they feared the personal consequences if they took a stance as whistleblowers. And none of us doubted that the airlines and aircraft manufacturers would do everything they could to fight back and keep the issue from exposure and recognition.

In the aftermath of that meeting, I decided to take a lead in setting up an association myself. I describe later in the book how the Aerotoxic Association took shape from that point onwards.

23

Victims in high places?

It was not by chance that the UCL researchers had tested pilots who had flown the BAe 146 or the Boeing 757; they were well known in the industry as the types of aircraft that experienced the most fume events. And there had been many incidents, including fatal accidents, involving these aircraft over the years. Typically these were attributed to 'fatigue' or 'pilot error'. It is beyond my resources to reopen the investigations, but it is worth noting that I am not aware of any occasion when the blame was placed on contaminated air. As a result, in spite of the known problems, these types of aircraft continued in service over a very long period.

To the best of my knowledge, there has also been no systematic research into what characteristics of these aircraft led to their particular problems; perhaps that is no wonder, if the problems were never formally identified. Both aircraft use similar models of APU, which are employed in a similar way in their start-up routines. I believe this is an issue which urgently calls for action.

Because the aircraft continue in use, not only do pilots continue to be affected by the fumes released, passengers too might receive worrying levels of exposure to organophosphates from the engine oil. It's interesting to note that all the senior members of the British Royal family, and senior members of successive UK governments too, flew regularly on the BAe 146 for twenty years. Lord Tyler (then Paul Tyler MP) noted in BALPA's 2005 conference papers that 'Prince Philip and Princess Anne are said to have complained of unpleasant fumes on flights in 2000.'

The most blatant example of a cover-up must be the allegation that BAe engineers added perfume to the APU oil to try to disguise the smell.

24

The Aerotoxic Association

Although I cannot claim to be the first to have campaigned on the issue of toxic air in aircraft, I am proud to have founded an association concerned with it, the Aerotoxic Association. It aims to provide support for affected aircrew and passengers; to coordinate information on research; to campaign for improvements on health and safety standards in the commercial airline industry; and to support known solutions.

The Aerotoxic Association is a UK limited company, funded by my own financial input only. I invested a large chunk of my

The formation of the Aerotoxic Association outside the Houses of Parliament, 18 June 2007.
Left to right: John Hoyte, Alan Carter, Susan Michaelis, Tristan Loraine, Len Lawrence, Trefor Mercer (now deceased), Andy Sawyers, Saeed Ashtiani, Julian Soddy.

loss of licence payment in helping to establish it. I have been chairman since its establishment.

We see our website (www.aerotoxic.org) as a core tool in our role as a campaigning organization. My aim has always been to keep the website as up to date, balanced, professional and factual as possible. We provide details or transcripts of papers from around the world that give both sides of the argument, so users can make their judgements on the evidence.

Until the Aerotoxic Association was founded, most of the political campaigning over issues of organophosphate poisoning had taken place in Australia. The Aviation Organo Phosphate Information Site had the slightly unfortunate acronym 'AOPIS', and I tried to find a more neutral name for our UK association.

We formally launched the Aerotoxic Association on 18 June 2007 at the Houses of Parliament, beneath the iconic tower housing Big Ben. In total there were around twenty grounded pilots at the launch, as well as family and friends. Another attendee was Samantha Sabatino (see Chapter 36), a passenger affected by aerotoxic syndrome.

25

Is there a cure?

I am not aware that there is any quick and failsafe cure for the symptoms of aerotoxic syndrome. But it is often the case that sufferers recover over time, and there are now a few doctors who specialize in neurological problems related to organophosphate exposure.

One of them is Dr Sarah Myhill, based in Wales, who had helped many affected sheep dippers before moving on to look at problems in aircrew. I saw her myself, and her basic advice was to 'Stop further exposure, eat well and sleep well.' I followed this myself, and though it took a full two years, I began to slowly recover. I hasten to add, though, that like many other sufferers I will never regain full fitness. Poor memory, temperature control and chemical sensitivity appear to be life-long symptoms for most.

Another is Dr Michel Mulder, a Dutchman who is both a medical doctor and former KLM pilot, so he is unusually well qualified to speak on the issue. And he also has first-hand experience of aerotoxic syndrome; he had to take medical retirement from his flying job as a result of ill-health.

Not only does Dr Mulder not fly commercial aircraft any more, he refuses to travel on them at all. He is in good company here; other determined non-flyers include his countryman, the famous footballer Dennis Bergkamp. It is not that he hates flying: far from it, he enjoys flying his own light aircraft, but like me he knows that bleed air makes him sick. He has pioneered a number of treatments, and has helped many sufferers improve their previously poor health.

26

How common is it?

By far the most common question from the media is 'How many people have suffered from aerotoxic syndrome?' I know it half-killed me and many others – but how can anyone put a sensible number on its frequency?

Here is an extract from 'Ill health following exposure to contaminated aircraft air: psychosomatic disorder or neurological injury?' This is a paper authored by Dr Sarah Mackenzie Ross, Dr Andrew Harper and Dr Jonathan Burdon in 2006.

> Given the low reporting rate of 3.66%, this could indicate that up to 1,967 flights in the UK may have experienced contaminated air events during 2004. If a modest passenger number of 100 per flight is assumed, over 196,000 passengers could potentially present to general physicians with symptoms of acute toxicity.[1]

Because there has been so little systematic research into aerotoxic syndrome, there are no answers as yet to many of the obvious questions, such as what the chances are of those exposed to organophosphates experiencing health problems as a result. I mentioned on page 8 that 'Don' took a DNA profile test, and it was suggested to him that he fell into a group covering 3 per cent of the population who are 'severely' affected. I myself am in what Dr Myhill describes as the 'third of the population [who] are poor detoxifiers of organophosphates' – and it nearly killed me. But this does not necessarily mean that only 3 per cent of those exposed develop symptoms. The anecdotal evidence, first from farm workers operating sheep dips and later from aircrew, suggests that the incidence level is much higher than this. (Of course, there might be variations in severity within a large group who all show some degree of susceptibility.)

My own experience certainly bears out a high level of

incidence. As well as meeting and hearing from many hundreds of sufferers worldwide, I have come across several in my own neighbourhood.

A friend living close to me in 2006, in a small Warwickshire village, was a former BA cabin crew member who had flown mostly on the Boeing 757. She had been grounded in around 2000 with complex neurological symptoms which baffled her consultant. We could make a fair guess at the cause.

Another near neighbour, Captain Keith Hicks, introduced me to another sufferer. When he watched a film Tristan Loraine had made, the mischievously titled *Welcome Aboard Toxic Airlines (WATA)*,[2] he recognized one of the interviewees as Captain David Hopkinson, a prematurely retired Boeing 757 BA pilot, with whom he had been on a flying course in the 1970s. Indeed, Captain Hopkinson deserves the credit for tipping off Tristan Loraine (his then BALPA union representative) about the problem, back in 2001.

Among the scientists who might in time be able to provide further information is Professor Clement ('Clem') Furlong, research professor in medicine and genome sciences at the University of Washington (USA). I met him together with my colleague Tony Watson (another former BAe 146 pilot who suffers from aerotoxic syndrome) in London in 2007, when he was in the United Kingdom for a visit. Professor Furlong has carried out considerable amounts of research on genetic suscep-

Poster for *Welcome Aboard Toxic Airlines* (2007), Tristan Loraine's documentary.
Source: Tristan Loraine.

tibility to organophosphate poisoning, and at the time of writing is working on identifying biomarkers to identify exposure to organophosphates in oil fumes. The aim is to be able to pinpoint not just whether, but also when, an individual was poisoned, enabling scientists to identify which particular fume event (that is, which specific flight) caused the poisoning of the aircrew or the passenger with a simple blood test.

As sufferers of aerotoxic syndrome, we were not best equipped to follow the science that Clem showed us on his laptop. Of course I welcome further research of this kind, but I also feel it embodies problems. It is all too easy for those resistant to action to demand higher and higher degrees of proof, more and more evidence of when and how someone was affected, and do nothing in the meantime. My view was, and still is, that we already have plenty of irrefutable evidence of aerotoxic syndrome. It is found in the documented cases of so many previously healthy people who travelled as passengers or aircrew on aircraft that are susceptible to the leakage of toxic chemicals into cabin air – through processes that are also well understood – and who afterwards experienced serious ill-health. Although it will be useful to know more about the syndrome, and to be able to put more precise figures to many aspects of it, the time for action is right now.

This stance was well summarized by a report on organophosphate poisoning, including case studies of airline pilots and passengers, sponsored by the Joseph Rowntree Trust and published on 20 January 2004 – when I was still flying the BAe 146. The report also covered people poisoned while serving as soldiers in the Gulf War, and agricultural workers exposed to organophosphates in sheep dips. It observed:

> Probably the most striking part of the OP [organophosphate] chemical saga is its relentless predictability. From the first warnings in 1951 about the dangers of OPs from Sir Solly Zuckerman right up to today's Gulf War inquiries in the United States and the UK, the pattern has been the same; warnings followed by more research leading to conclusions which beget more research and more warnings before the cycle begins again.
>
> Prove that OPs poison people, say the companies which manufacture these chemicals – and politicians often say the

same thing. That is why there is so much research, revisiting the tiniest findings from previous work which might prove or disprove part of the drama. But why? If someone is shot, do scientists spend years trying to work out the trajectory of the bullet, the make of the weapon, or the circumstances in which the trigger was pulled rather than treating the wounded person and trying to prevent more fighting?[3]

'Ginger Jake'

Another historic incidence of organophosphate poisoning – and a rather intriguing one – occurred in the United States back in the late 1920s and early 1930s. It figured in two 1930 recordings by blues musicians, Ishman Bracey's 'Jake Liquor Blues' and Tommy Johnson's 'Alcohol and Jake Blues'.

They were singing about a phenomenon called 'Jake leg' or the 'Jake walk', which musicians had realized – before the medical profession caught up with them – was suffered by those who had drunk a concoction called 'Jamaica Ginger'. This was sold as a medicine, but that was a thin disguise for the fact that it was an alcoholic drink, popular in many poor communities in the US South. To get around Prohibition, its producers included an organophosphate additive, tricresyl phosphate, to try to cheat the government's tests. What they didn't know was that tricresyl phosphate is a slow-acting neurotoxin that affects the neurons that control movement among other effects.

Doctors described the Jake leg condition – although they had yet to identify its cause – in the *New England Journal of Medicine* in June 1930. The toxin starts by causing lower leg muscular pain and tingling, followed by muscle weakness in the arms and legs. The effect on the legs caused a distinctive form of muscle paralysis that required affected people to lift their legs high during walking to allow their feet to clear the ground.

Jamaica Ginger was not banned because of these disastrous health effects, but by the Food and Drug Administration (FDA) who cottoned on that it was an alcoholic drink in rather poor disguise.[4]

27

A cover-up

It is no secret that both aircraft manufacturers and airlines have done their best to stifle debate and information on aerotoxic syndrome. Here is a particularly blatant example.

On 13 August 2007, Senator Kerry O'Brien revealed in the Australian Parliament a document dated 3 September 1993, in which British Aerospace agreed a cash payment to Ansett Airlines and East-West Airlines in respect of potential claims relating to toxins in cabin air. He reminded senators of the findings of the Senate inquiry some seven years earlier (see page 86), and pointed out that there seemed to be double standards in play. There was a strict regime on testing airline pilots for drugs and alcohol, but no consistent system to check on the quality of the air they breathed when at work.

He told the Senate:

> Earlier today the Senate gave passage to a bill which provides for the Civil Aviation Safety Authority to administer a new drug and alcohol testing regime for the aviation industry .... But the regulator appears not to understand that it is not just the consumption of drugs and alcohol by safety-sensitive personnel that imperils aviation safety. The introduction of toxic fumes into the cabin environment presents a clear and present danger for everyone on board an aircraft ....
>
> Last July I asked the government about its knowledge of payments made under an agreement between British Aerospace and Ansett Airlines and East-West Airlines in connection with design flaws in the BAe 146 aircraft – flaws which resulted in contamination of cabin air by oil and other fumes. In reply, the minister told me that he was aware of a question about these alleged payments being asked in the House of Lords but disavowed knowledge of any agreement. The minister also refused my request to investigate the existence of any such agreement.
>
> Subsequent to [this] ... I have become aware of documents

that suggest that money did indeed change hands in return for silence on aircraft defects producing toxic fumes. The first document is titled 'Agreement' and is dated 3 September 1993. The parties to this purported agreement are British Aerospace Regional Aircraft Ltd, East-West Airlines and Ansett Transport Industries. It notes that BAe warranted that the aircraft it supplied would be free from defects due to defective workmanship or defective design. It says:

> *'Ansett and EWA have made certain written claims against BAe alleging defective design of the aircraft resulting in the production of obnoxious oil and other (the 'cabin environment problem') fumes affecting the passenger cabins of some or all of the aircraft.*
>
> *Following certain discussions and negotiations the parties hereto have agreed to settle such claims upon and subject to the terms and conditions hereinafter contained.*
>
> *BAe hereby agrees with Ansett and with EWA that it shall pay to EWA the sum of Australian $750,000 .... Ansett and EWA hereby jointly and severally agree that the said sum of A$750,000 shall be paid by BAe to EWA as liquidated damages in full and final settlement of any and all claims which Ansett or EWA may have against BAe either now or in the future in respect of oil or other fumes adversely affecting the cabin environment.'*

Senator O'Brien added:

> This document then says that the parties agree to split proceeds from any joint settlement reached with the manufacturers of the auxiliary power units. The document concludes with a confidentiality clause.[1]

He also gave details, from the leaked documents, of another agreement, between the two airlines and Allied Signal, covering claims for fume leaks from auxiliary power units, and worth A$1.25 million, again with a confidentiality clause. In the light of the revelations emerging from these documents, he complained that the Senate appeared to have been misled by aviation industry representatives at the hearings during the Senate inquiry in 1999–2001.

Senator O'Brien's statement showed that a decade before the

fume event that I suffered in a BAe 146, the aircraft's manufacturer had set aside a substantial amount of money to settle claims from those suffering ill health. It does not realistically leave any doubt that BAe (now part of BAE Systems) knew it was poisoning me and others.

28

The experiences of relatives: a widow and a divorcee tell their tales

Lingering suspicions: a widow's tale – Diana Blanden

My husband Richard joined BOAC in 1966 and retired from British Airways in 1999. He had 33 years' service, initially on VC10s and Boeing 747s, then the Trident, and from 1985 to 1999 he flew 757s and 767s. I pulled his medical records from his doctor; as next of kin you are permitted to do so. I have them to send to a professor in the United States. The very fact that he gave his brain and spinal cord to medical research indicates he didn't have any problem sharing his body parts for the purposes of research. I spoke to the motor neurone disease (MND)[1] consultant after he had died. I said to him, is there any reason why we couldn't use his brain and spinal cord to check for TCP [tri-cresyl phosphate] poisoning? He initially said no, he thought it was too late, but as soon as he understood that I didn't have an ulterior motive, that I didn't want to sue, he investigated further and said, 'Yes, we could do that, but we would have to use a bona fide company.' Of course I would want that too. He obviously didn't want to get involved in litigation – but research, that's a different matter.

MND: why did he get it? When Richard was diagnosed, there were no known reasons. Often, quite fit and able people get it. Also, it is thought that some chemicals can induce it.

To go back to where we were: on his 50th birthday he said that he wasn't sure he could continue to fly until retirement – he didn't feel quite as sharp as he used to. He decided that he would continue, at a slower pace. He bid for the minimum trips, and preferred to start work in the afternoon, when he felt his brain function was better. He couldn't cope with other pressures, and he slept a lot. He kept saying things would be different when he retired. But things weren't different; he got worse. He retired at 55. He didn't take well to retirement: he became morose, depressed, and could not motivate himself. We put that down to losing the uniform, when in retirement no one wants to know you. We didn't make him feel like that.

He had an Internet affair, which nearly ended our marriage. That behaviour was bizarre – he was very family-oriented. He handed over a large sum of money to this person in America. It was completely out of character. He was very needy, tearful and emotional. He did work at a Citizen's Advice Bureau – IT work. He was very clever. It was as a volunteer, one day a week. But he couldn't keep up with the interaction with the staff – so he worked in the evenings when no one was there. He would take a very long time to do anything. He left without notice. We didn't know what was going on. We just thought he was being a grumpy old man, but on reflection this was the beginning of MND. The MND website does list bizarre behaviours as symptoms.

I am a counsellor, and worked for a charity. Richard became an IT support volunteer. He seemed better able to cope with the interaction if it came through me. It was very strange for a man who was very competent. When I look back, it was really weird: we were refurbishing a couple of flats that we owned, and he kept falling out with the contractors. He put barriers in place; made it difficult for them; wouldn't answer questions – but we now know that his brain wasn't functioning properly. He didn't want to lose face, so his way was to rubbish the contractors. Also, he found it difficult to follow conversations. We would be having lunch, and he couldn't follow the conversation. He also became paranoid. We had a large garden at the time, and at the bottom there were playing fields, where the kids would hang out in the evenings. He was always thinking that they were going to break in. He would want me to telephone the headmaster to complain – he wasn't able to do that himself. He got things completely out of perspective.

Then his mother died. She was 97: it was expected, and very peaceful. He couldn't handle this; it was so difficult for him. He did the probate of her affairs. She only had a house, nothing else, but it took him nine months to do this.

He never went to the doctor for depression; he avoided doctors.

[What prompted him eventually to go?] He got heart palpitations, and that frightened him. The GP sent him to a cardiologist, who said his heart was absolutely fine. Then the cardiologist suggested a neurologist. That's when it all kicked off. He died in February 2011; he had been diagnosed in March 2010 with motor neurone desease with frontal lobe dementia. He had lots of tests prior to that final diagnosis; they don't give a MND diagnosis straight away, it is a death sentence, so they test everything. In one test, a cognitive test, he had to say as many words as he could think of beginning with the letter 'F', and he could only think of five. This was someone who read avidly. That's when we thought something was terribly, terribly wrong and I began to think: is there something poisoning the brain?

Richard was one of the first pilots to have flown 33 years in jet-engined aircraft. We discovered that a colleague of his had the same diagnosis and have since heard of a third pilot who has died of MND. You think, what's going on here? The consultant was very dismissive of the suggestion that there was a link. What convinced me? I suppose I have to be honest, I can't be convinced because there is no evidence, but I have a very strong feeling, and also Richard knew something about this, because I remember an incident in the car. Our car broke down about 20 miles from home – this was around 2005. He was paranoid and said, 'Close the window, the fumes from the exhaust could poison us!' On his walk-around on the aircraft he would always put a handkerchief over his mouth and nose. He was aware that there was a problem. Richard was also paranoid about smoke. Before the smoking ban, he wouldn't sit next to people smoking in a restaurant. As a pilot, in the early days, he would keep the 'no smoking' sign on much longer than he was supposed to.

My goal, and Richard would want this, is to have his brain and spinal cord tested for TCP poisoning. If nothing is found that would be fine – at least we would know. Is there any evidence to suggest that these tiny toxins can build up over time in people who are unable to process them and you don't see the devastating results until many years later? My view is, it's possible, although I will have to leave this question and the answers to the experts.

Richard didn't smoke, didn't drink, didn't carry extra weight. He wasn't super-sporty but he kept himself fit. There was nothing to suggest that he contributed to it. When you talk to the MND doctors, they do say it just happens that way.

A traumatized pilot's wife: 'Erin Sierra'

My husband Mike flew as a first officer for BA, having been accepted on their sponsorship programme fresh out of the Navy at 23, and started on the Airbus A319 and A320 in 2000. After a few years he experienced a great deal of fatigue, so reduced his hours to a part-time 75 per cent contract. In 2009 Mike started to lose weight, suffered from muscle spasms and insomnia. In order to quieten his mind he listened to a lot of spiritual podcasts and became more and more immersed in searching for spiritual enlightenment.

In October 2009 he made a mistake on the flight deck, nothing serious, the captain picked it up but it caused Mike to look at his health. He signed himself off sick. Doctors could not understand his illness, then a few months later we heard an interview with John Hoyte on Radio 4 and he had blood tests done. High (very high) nickel and benzene. The Toxicology Unit at Guys Hospital were of course in denial it was linked to flying.

In July 2010 he left me (and our daughter,) stating a spiritual reason, that I was not enlightened. The following years have seen a real mental deterioration, delusional behaviour, excess spending of his lump sums, and being criminally charged for breaking into our house with an axe back in March. Sadly when he was in custody they were unable to section him [compulsory detention under UK mental health legislation], because Mike's illness does not fall into the usual sectionable illnesses.

So he still lives as a recluse in our village in a five-bed house that he has not paid rent on since August 2013 (his landlady communicates with me) and is soon to be evicted. His lump sums are spent. He cannot see his daughter because of the three-year restraining order he was issued with in court last May. We are currently still classed as high risk in case he breaks in again.

29

Balance?

One problem that we share with climate change campaigners, and campaigners in many other fields, is the determination of the media, and particularly publicly funded media, to be 'balanced' in their coverage. Even when well over 90 per cent of scientists agree that climate change is already taking place, the BBC feel they must provide this 'balance' by hunting out a dissenting scientist to put the opposite point of view. For obvious reasons, in the case of aerotoxic syndrome airlines and aircraft manufacturers are only too eager to provide their own 'balance' to the information disseminated by campaigners who want to see aerotoxic syndrome recognized, its sufferers recompensed and its causes removed.

In October 2007 Tristan Loraine called me excitedly to say that a BBC *Panorama* production team had been in touch. They were researching a programme on air quality issues in airliners for this, probably the most prestigious television documentary programme in the United Kingdom. A thirty-minute programme presented by Jerry Northam was broadcast in April 2008.

What a disappointment that was! Although the producers and researchers had been in direct contact, it did not even mention the word 'aerotoxic', let alone give publicity to the Aerotoxic Association. It did include interviews with Neils Gomer, the pilot in the 1999 Malmo incident (see page 83), Samantha Sabatino, Dr Sarah Mackenzie Ross and others, but their evidence of the serious issues of toxins in airlines was 'balanced' by interviews with airline representatives, BALPA (which had reversed its initial conclusions) and aircraft manufacturer representatives who played down the dangers to the point of denying them.

For me, this was further evidence not just of the determination of the industry not to acknowledge the problem, but of the difficulty of persuading the media and politicians to take aerotoxicity seriously in the face of their lobbying.

I should emphasize that this is not just my personal opinion, but was widely shared by others. For example, David Learmount, safety editor of *Flight International*, sent me an email which said:

> Panorama didn't do the subject. I took part in their research. I know what they knew, and then I saw what they actually aired. It was hopeless, and I don't know why. Were the journalists scared off by threats from lawyers? It's all I can think of. They had the real stuff, it was public domain stuff, and they didn't use it. I've not been able to take Panorama seriously since then.[1]

30

The deniers

As evidence mounted of the impact of cabin air fumes on the health of flight crew and passengers, pressure grew for more studies and official inquiries. In 2007 there were two major official reports published in the United Kingdom.

The first was a report by the Committee on Toxicity (COT) on an enquiry that it had carried out from 2005, following pressure from the trade unions TGWU (the Transport General Workers Union) and BALPA.[1] I would describe its conclusions as evasive and complacent. It repeated phrases such as 'there is no evidence ...'. The trade unions objected to the lack of transparency in the process. Some individuals protested that the COT Secretariat misrepresented information that had been provided to the Committee, in such a way as to disguise or downplay the hazards posed by fumes. For example the Australian clinical and forensic psychologist Leonie Coxon, who had carried out research on aircrew affected by cabin air toxins, had found 'mild to moderate/severe and severe/significant impairment' in the aircrew she had tested, yet the COT reported that her work had revealed only subtle changes in cognitive performance.

AOPIS produced an eighteen-page report detailing what it concluded were serious errors and misrepresentations, including a downplaying of hazards revealed in the UK Contaminated Air Database.[2] In addition, Susan Michaelis and other academics and experts produced an eleven-page critique detailing these and other shortcomings of the COT report. The IPA stated that it judged the 'misinterpretations of the evidence put forward' to be 'deliberate, and designed to minimize and mitigate the changes required to achieve closure of the cabin air contamination problem'.[3]

The second report was by a House of Lords special committee.[4] Again, it could hardly ignore the building mountain of evidence of toxicity problems, but it certainly seemed to try its best to do so. Its most interesting feature was that it reported a significant admission by Boeing. As I explained earlier, Boeing's 787 Dreamliner has a cabin air intake system that does not involve bleed air. The manufacturer claims that is because of fuel efficiency, and is careful to avoid mentioning that this design change has anything to do with the pollution problems associated with bleed air. But Boeing's written evidence to the House of Lords in 2007 gave a more candid view:

> The Boeing 787 will have a no-bleed architecture for the outside air supply to the cabin. This architecture eliminates the risk of engine oil decomposition products from being introduced in the cabin supply air in the rare event of a failed engine compressor seal. In addition, this architecture improves fuel efficiency, thus reducing fuel burn and associated engine emissions.[5]

In the past few years of campaigning on the subject, I have been struck by the markedly different conclusions that different authors and researchers reach from broadly the same evidence base. For some researchers, strong and consistent correlations between toxins leaking into cabin air and reports of serious ill-health have been a cause of concern, even alarm, while others seek every opportunity to downplay the risks. This shows that we are dealing not only with science, but also with politics.

But let me make it clear: there should not need to be absolute certainty that harm is being caused before airline management take action. Management does not only depend on evidence, it also involves such concepts as judgement, values and a duty of care towards employees. Even if the evidence base was very much weaker than it is, aviation employers should still have taken far more precautions than they have over the past decades to ensure a healthy environment for their staff and for passengers, given the known toxicity of the substances that are on board aircraft.

Assessment by deniers

As well as learning this history of denial and dismissal of proven problems as a campaigner, I had a personal experience of it in July 2010. By May 2008 I felt sufficiently well again that I passed my class one medical. I was obviously keen not to be made seriously ill again by further toxic air exposures, and asked the CAA to limit my medical to 'non pressurized' aircraft only.

As well as wanting to be able to fly again, something I have always loved, I felt the need to set the record straight. Now that I knew about aerotoxic syndrome, and had tested positive for toxins that were linked to fume events in the aircraft I was flying, I wanted it on record that this was the cause of my earlier health problems, and for the CAA, as regulators, to take responsibility for my future passengers' welfare. I had only made a recovery after having pursued a course of treatment based on a correct diagnosis, and I wanted the diagnoses of 'stress' and 'depression' to be effectively struck off the record.

If I was not subject to mental problems unrelated to toxins, then there was no reason why I should not fly unpressurized aircraft. Re-exposure to toxins found in pressurized aircraft would certainly bring my illness back again. This has happened to people I know and is definitely to be avoided.

The CAA verdict was that the unpressurized aircraft limitation could not be applied. I decided to appeal against this judgement. The minutes of my CAA appeal hearing make it apparent how little my assessors welcomed this argument.[6] There is a clumsy contradiction at the heart of their verdict. The panel accepted the premise that if it could be shown that my illness had been caused by fume events, there would be a case for reinstatement of a licence for non-pressurized aircraft. But it rejected an application from my solicitor to consider information on cabin air studies 'as it has no bearing on the appeal question'.

The written summary of the panel hearing on 6 July 2010 seemed to me almost comically biased. I had presented medical opinions on my condition from five experienced clinicians. They all testified that I had suffered a serious industrial injury. It arose from a known hazard – exposure to toxic fumes – and there was objective evidence in the forms of the elevated levels of the toxic substances in my body. The CAA – the enforcing body for health and safety law for aviation in the United Kingdom – made a derogatory comment questioning the validity of the judgement of every one of these experts.

For example it said (of evidence from Professor Abou-Donia) 'The significance of the tests cited was not clear to the Panel';

(of Dr Nicola Hembry) 'The Panel had concerns regarding the sufficiency of the evidence cited'; and (of Biolab) 'The Panel had concerns regarding the validity of these reports'. The Panel also heard from experts (whose evidence was not put forward by me) who disagreed with this diagnosis and ascribed my illness to psychological causes. It made no comment at all on their diagnoses. It reminded me of the parody by the late comedian Peter Cook of a judge's summing up to a jury. It concluded with the immortal phrase, 'You are now to retire, carefully to consider your verdict of not guilty.'

You will note from the quotes above that the CAA report did not give reasons for doubting the distinguished experts whose opinions I had presented. While I was writing this book, my researcher asked the CAA press office for a full scientific explanation. It declined to provide any further evidence at all. The CAA claimed it could not breach my medical confidentiality, which was absurd since I had given formal permission for the information to be released. These were the proceedings of a public body with a vital statutory function. I think this refusal was shocking.

It should be borne in mind too that Regulation 6 of the UK law on Control of Substances Hazardous to Health clearly puts the onus on the employer to manage a known risk, not on an employee to prove that harm has resulted from it.

More failure to report

Of course, if reports on incidents are not filed, there is not even a verdict to be questioned. I described earlier how I had submitted a mandatory occurrence report (MOR) in 2004 after Flybe decided not to submit one on an incident that I felt certainly warranted it. I was not alone.

In 2007 another Flybe captain told me what happened when he experienced a fume event aboard a BAe 146 a few weeks earlier. It seemed to both of us to have been a serious fume event, and afterwards he had taken all his crew to hospital for tests. He filed an air safety report (ASR) with Flybe management, but the management concluded that the event need not be reported to the CAA.

This is a part of this report (with the names removed) which

Flybe's internal management decided was too trivial to warrant official reporting:

> On reflection *** seemed vague and was moving more deliberately and slowly that usual, *** looked exhausted; her eyes looked to be almost closed as she ate her breakfast; *** was just standing at row 1 – she would normally have been busying herself with something at this stage if not in conversation. Something was different about the demeanour of each member of my crew, and I was feeling like an observer, as if I was not really there. I asked each crew member in turn how they were feeling, within earshot of the others admittedly, *** said that she felt exhausted and her legs felt heavy, she had been early to bed the night before and was surprised to be feeling so washed out. *** said that she had been tired generally but had gone to bed early in anticipation of being called from stand-by and so was also surprised to be feeling so tired after two quiet sectors, *** considered my question and appeared a little confused, he said he was very tired. I said I felt spaced out and detached from the situation. He said something along the lines of, oh you mean that feeling, yes me too.[7]

A union caves in

One organization to which pilots with sickness problems naturally look for advice and support is their trade union, BALPA. On 20 and 21 April 2005 it hosted a major conference on Contaminated Air Protection, Air Safety and Cabin Air Quality at Imperial College, London. At its conclusion BALPA issued a statement. Among the signatories were BALPA general secretary Jim McAuslan and sixteen distinguished scientists who had published papers on the subject:

> We wish to bring to the urgent attention of Government, Aviation Regulators and the Airline and Aerospace industry the following conclusions, distilled from the conference. There is a workplace problem resulting in chronic and acute illness amongst flight crew (both pilots and cabin crew). The workplace in which these illnesses are being induced is the aircraft cabin environment. This, we conclude, is resulting

> in significant flight safety issues, in addition to unacceptable flight crew personnel health implications. Further, we are concerned the passengers may also be suffering from similar symptoms to those exhibited by flight crew. We urgently call upon Government, Industry and Regulators to work in partnership with cabin environment medical and analyst specialists and representatives from flight crew unions to analyse, quantify and remedy the cabin air quality problems that we have identified exist.[8]

Strong stuff. But in 2014, BALPA's website made this statement about reported ill-health from toxins in cabin air:

> We have yet to see consistent, credible and viable evidence of a robust nature which meet scientific criteria and would hold up to scrutiny in a court of law.[9]

(Note that BALPA have since amended this statement to remove 'and would hold up to scrutiny in a court of law'.)

Does the evidence meet scientific criteria? I do not think there is any serious doubt that it does. Would it hold up in a court of law? Perhaps that is the issue that got BALPA, and many others, running scared. We shall look later at whether the evidence has indeed done so.

Two unions have been set up as rivals to BALPA in the United Kingdom: the Independent Pilots Association and the Professional Pilots Union. Both have been far more supportive of the issue than BALPA. The PPU is quite new at the time of writing, set up in 2012 and only available to employees of Virgin Atlantic. The primary cause of the split was a disagreement over a pay deal at Virgin, but the new union takes a much more robust stance on behalf of pilots suffering from toxic injury from fume events. Its website guidance reports that medical studies 'have identified adverse short and long term effects to health' from cabin air-quality events.

And biased summaries

As part of my campaigning activities I joined the London-based Air Safety Group (ASG), which is mainly composed of retired aviation industry professionals who still want to be involved with safety matters. In June 2008 I was invited to participate in a debate about aerotoxic syndrome for the Parliamentary Advisory Council for Transport Safety (PACTS). I was pitched against Dr Ken Edgington, also of the ASG, who had previously been chief medical officer at BA. Of course, I suggested that there was clear and overwhelming evidence for aerotoxic syndrome. Dr Edgington argued that the evidence was inconclusive. The audience, which included Professor Bagshaw (the doctor who had grounded me with 'chronic stress' in 2006) and a BALPA representative, seemed to me placid and uninterested. You can read the summary of the debate in the PACTS annual report.[10] It dismisses our case as being made up of mere 'beliefs 'and 'possibilities'. There is no serious consideration of the huge amount of evidence in medical records and independent research that I had presented.

31

The deniers denied

The aerospace division of the Society of Automotive Engineers reviewed similar evidence to that considered by the COT and the House of Lords in 2007 (as outlined in the last chapter), but instead of effectively giving the practice of bleed air the all-clear, it sounded a more sober, warning note. It concluded that even at low concentrations airborne chemicals may adversely affect crew and passenger comfort, and that 'Increased contamination levels from leaks or equipment wear or failure may affect occupant comfort, health and flight safety.' These conclusions are similar to the warnings made by Dr Sarah Mackenzie Ross of University College London in 2006 (see page 92), and indeed many others.

It helped that the chair of the SAE aerospace committee on Aircraft Environmental Systems was Dr Jean-Christophe Balouet, an environmental scientist who works with the United Nations and Interpol, and is one of the three scientists to develop the concept of aerotoxic syndrome. He has been a colleague and supporter of the campaign.

32

Case study: Julian Soddy

I first heard of Captain Julian Soddy when he was put forward as a potential non-medical assessor for my loss of licence payment in 2005. Only later did I realize that this former RAF fast jet and BAe 146 pilot was also a sufferer from aerotoxic syndrome himself.

Julian got a clue to what had made him ill much earlier than I did, purely because of a coincidence. In 2000 he consulted a GP whose father, a sheep farmer in Wales, had been affected by sheep-dip syndrome. As a result the doctor recognized his symptoms, and referred him to Dr Goran Jamal, a pioneer in the study of organophosphate (OP) poisoning, who confirmed the diagnosis. He had already been off work for about three months, but this led to his being grounded for good. He estimates it cost him about half a million pounds in salary. Although, like me, he was given compensation for the loss of his flying licence, and he received a pension, these together did not even make up for his financial loss, let alone provide any compensation for the health problems he was suffering.

Julian blames his problems not on a single large 'fume event', but on his daily experience on the BAe 146s, which was much like mine. As he told the authorities who reviewed his case:

> I went back to flying the 146 in 1995 and frequently when we started the engines up from cold in the morning the auxiliary power units would belch out smoke into the cockpit. We just turned the air conditioning up to maximum to try to burn off the oil. ... My view is that this is an insidious, long-term effect which creeps up on you over time.[1]

Before this, Captain Soddy had been grounded for about three months and his health was reviewed every four weeks. He says:

> I wanted to return to flying. The chief medical officer of the

> Civil Aviation Authority (CAA) is a friend of mine, and I told him I wanted to fly. The airline bent over backwards to help, and I went back to flying with a colleague. But after about eight weeks, the same symptoms came back and I was almost in a vegetable type state.[2]

After seeing his local doctor and Dr Jamal, Captain Soddy was grounded for good. He dismisses as next to useless the CAA advice at the time, that crew should use their oxygen masks. 'I had severe flu-like symptoms every time I flew and they just became worse', he remembered. 'As we climbed through about 10,000 feet, my head would be bunged up, I had headaches and shortness of breath. In the end, I had to go back to the toilet and breathe deeply to bring myself back round.' Like many pilots, he had been a fitness fanatic, but he had to give up his usual game of squash after he had been exposed to the fumes.

He feels the BAe 146's problems are the result of its design:

> The space within the aeroplane made it difficult to put in the recycling type of air filters and so air filtration was very poor. In addition, the auxiliary power units were difficult to maintain.

He also drew my attention to another chemical problem, affecting even aircraft without these design problems; fumes from de-icing fluid sprayed on to the aircraft, which could easily pass into the jet intakes.[3] As he put it, 'There are more pilots around than there are jobs, so people are not keen to talk. But I think this is a much bigger issue than people realize.'

Not only did Julian share his views on the problems with the BAe 146 with the authorities, he also appeared on the BBC *Panorama* 2008 report and in Tristan Loraine's documentary, *Welcome Aboard Toxic Airlines*.

33

The Cranfield study

I have already mentioned a research project carried out at Cranfield University. It is important to this story because it is frequently cited by those who claim there is 'no evidence' for aerotoxic syndrome, such as Baroness Kramer's quote on pages 79–80. So it is worth looking at this research, to see how it came to those conclusions – or at least, conclusions that could be taken in this way.

Professor Helen Muir – who had sadly died before the research was completed – was the initial lead researcher in this project, which was announced in 2008. Its final report (which I call here the Muir report) was published in May 2011.[1] The report summary stated that there was 'no evidence of pollutants occurring in cabin air at levels exceeding available health and safety standards and guidelines'. Grateful industry spokespeople seized on the findings – or rather, this particular sentence out of them – and have repeated it many times since. I have no doubt that many people, including senior politicians, sincerely believe that the Cranfield study 'proved' that there was no issue that called for further investigation.

Is that in fact the case? Let us take a good look at the Muir report. What did its research consist of, how was it paid for, and what did it actually find?

The account I present here is indebted not least to academics from Cranfield itself. Jeremy Ramsden, Cranfield's chair of nanotechnology, has been particularly helpful to us in unravelling the issues that the Muir research reveals (or in many ways, tries to hide). In particular, he staged a one-day workshop on the issues which was held at Cranfield University on 11 October 2011. The organizational work was done by Christine Standing on behalf of Collegium Basilea, a Swiss-based independent academic research institute.[2] I draw on it heavily in what follows.

The objectives of the research, according to the Muir report's own summary, were:

> To analyse cabin air for volatile organic compounds (VOCs), semi-volatile organic compounds (SVOCs), particles and carbon monoxide (CO) in normal operations during all phases of flight (eg climb, cruise, descent), and to detect and characterise any anomalous elevations of VOC, SVOC and particle concentrations during any 'fume events' or 'air quality events'.[3]

To do this, the researchers took a sample of 100 flights. This comprised twenty flights each on five different models of aircraft; the BAe 146, the Boeing 757 (both aircraft known to be more prone to fume events), and the Airbus A319, A320, A321. They did not pick these flights at random from charter holiday flights or scheduled flights; the flights to be monitored were selected in conjunction with the airlines. So we can safely assume that these were flights where the crew and maintenance staff knew monitoring was to take place, and were conscious that this was not the time to cut corners. It seems likely to me too that because of the way the research was set up, there were no known 'Old Stinky' aircraft among the sample.

Crew members noted minor smells or fumes on thirty-eight of these flights, which I am sure you will agree is a significant proportion. The report stated that 'No fume events occurred during these flights that triggered the airline's protocols for formal reporting of incidents.' This is a conclusion that has been challenged, as I shall discuss. But even if the 'airline's protocols' did not require reporting of any of these fume events, that certainly does not mean there were none. It merely means these fell into the massive class of unreported fume events.

But note, it can hardly be denied that major fume events do occur from time to time. I have described a number of them in this book. However, *the Muir research did not involve any of them*. It is rather like an accident investigation unit carrying out research into plane crashes on the basis of a sample that did not include a single plane that crashed. To conclude on the basis of the sample that planes never crash would be ridiculous; everyone knows that aircraft *do* very occasionally crash. It is equally laughable to suggest that the Muir research could conclude, on the basis of a fairly small sample that did not include any major fume events, that there *are* no major fume events, or that those that do occur do not present problems of toxicity.

Indeed, in 2007 the UK government claimed that fume events are rare.[4] The government also claimed that because of the unpredictable nature of fume events, it was impossible to measure the concentrations of chemicals being released during such events. Unpredictable? They only needed to ask me, or any other BAe 146 pilot. *We could have induced a visible fume event on the ground any time they asked us to*. I wrote to Professor Helen Muir on 6 November 2007, offering to do just that. She thanked me for my offer but told me she had a pilot on her staff and my help was not required.

Professor Ramsden obtained copies through Freedom of Information requests of academic peer reviews of the research methods. These had not previously been made public by Cranfield University, or even made available to its own academic staff, or to the UK government, which had sponsored the research. I'm sure that suited both bodies, since the reviewers had some highly critical comments to make. These reviews were carried out before the final research report was published, but I am not aware that any of their comments led to changes in the final report.

Roy Harrison, professor of environmental health at the University of Birmingham, was one of these reviewers. He looked at the method the researchers had used for gauging levels of contaminants. This involved pumping air through stainless steel sorbent tubes packed with quartz wool and Tenax TA (the brand name of a porous polymer resin used for trapping airborne organic compounds). Professor Harrison described this method as 'fairly standard' for volatile organic compounds, but 'wholly untested' for organophosphate esters, and for semi-volatile compounds more generally. Organophosphate esters are highly polar compounds, and Tenax is a substance designed to trap apolar molecules.[5] This is a very important point, because semi-volatile organic compounds are at the core of the problem. Organophosphate esters themselves are one of the main contaminants that cause ill-health amongst aircrew and frequent flyers. So, in Professor Harrison's words, 'There is every reason to believe that the Tenax tubes are likely to be markedly inefficient for the sampling of OP esters and consequently the lack of sampling efficiency studies conducted on airborne samples is a very serious deficiency.'[6] In other words, if the researchers didn't find OP esters, it could have been because they used equipment that wasn't capable of finding them. It is not that there is no acknowledged efficient method of collecting OP esters; indeed the Muir report itself referred to the use of SPE (solid phase extraction) cartridges as being more suitable for the purpose.[7] But this was not the equipment the researchers themselves made use of.

Another point made by Professor Harrison was on the analysis of ultrafine particles. These tiny particles are generally regarded as a potentially serious air pollution problem, because they are so readily absorbed by those who breathe air containing them.

The Muir report noted that:

> Mean ultrafine particle numbers (all flight sectors) were always in the range 1,000–100,000 particles per cm^{-3}. On five flight sectors peak concentrations exceeded the maximum range of the instrument (500,000 particles per cm^{-3}).[8]

The researchers benchmarked this against other workplaces, and the second-highest concentration found was 400,000 particles per cm^{-3} for a kitchen with tortilla ovens. So the level in the aircraft was exceptionally high, indeed so high that the instruments could not capture it accurately. Did the researchers find some way of measuring this concentration using instruments capable of doing so? To the best of my knowledge, they did not.

Professor Harrison also wrote, 'Some explanation for the source of ultrafine particles, and consideration of accompanying pollutants, would be well worthwhile.'[9] If this extraordinary concentration was found in a study concerned entirely with pollution, I would have thought this not only 'worthwhile', but absolutely essential. Even so, it does not appear to have been done.

A third criticism that Professor Harrison made was that no reason was given for the selection of chemicals tested for. The list was comparatively short. It ran to just eight substances, out of the dozens, potentially hundreds, of hydrocarbons and their pyrolyzed by-products, some of them highly toxic, that earlier studies suggest might be regularly present in cabin air. What you do not look for, you do not find. So the research told us nothing at all about the presence of the majority of the polluting chemicals that have been found in the air inside these airliners, although the participating researchers did state at the COT meeting on 17 September 2013 in which the Muir report was discussed that the chromatograms used to identify and quantify the eight substances were still available and could be re-analysed to search for other contaminants.

Another peer review, also obtained for this book through a Freedom of Information request, was carried out by Dr Peter Jackson. He too drew attention to the failure to analyse a fume event. He wrote:

> It is important to stress that its results have little bearing on the exposure to VOCs [volatile organic compounds] and SVOCs [semi-volatile organic compounds] in reportable fume events, the basis of the suggested second component [of the research].[10]

He was also critical of the limited number of potential contaminants tested for, and the lack of information given about the criteria for their selection.

An article in 2008 in the journal of the UK Royal Society for the Prevention of Accidents also drew attention to chemicals that were not tested for in the Muir research.[11] These included some of the isomers of tricresyl phosphate that are either more toxic, or are present in higher concentrations in jet engine oil than those looked for. Another highly toxic component of engine oil is N-phenyl-α-naphthylamine, known by the abbreviation PAN. This is a known carcinogen. It was not tested for in the Muir study.

I also interviewed David Learmount, veteran flight safety correspondent and senior editor at *Flight International*, for this book. He had looked at some detail into the Muir research, both during and after it took place, and he told me he considered the Cranfield Cabin Air Survey report to be 'worthless. It is without value or validity.'[12]

David made the point even before the 100 flights took off that it would be impossible to draw meaningful conclusions from them if they did not involve any significant fume events. He also explained further about those 'minor' events that were effectively dismissed:

> I was one of the journalists invited up to Cranfield at the time of the programme. ... They told me and other journalists that there were some fume events on the first couple of flights, in the cockpit; whether these registered I really don't know .... at the time we were advised that they had taken place – by voice. I assumed that when the report came out, that it would report the fume events, so I was pretty surprised when it didn't.[13]

At a media briefing, presenters told journalists about the problems of different methods of capture and measurement of contaminants. David recalled:

> The impression I was under during the briefing was that they were giving us all the downsides of all of them. I thought: 'This is being presented to us as all about the downsides, so the results are meaningless.' It sounded like a pessimistic way to start – that they are going to capture and measure, but the systems are not very good; that there are limitations.[14]

So to summarize, the opinion of experts on the Muir research seems to be that it was all but designed to fail. It looked only for major events that were unlikely to happen, and indeed did not happen. It looked only for a small selection of the chemicals that might cause health problems, and it looked for these in ways that were acknowledged to have problems and limitations. What's more, when the researchers came across minor fume events that might have provided at least some useful information, they apparently decided to write them off as not worth detailed investigation.

Another problem with the Muir report is that the use of ground-based workplace and domestic environments as benchmarks is not valid. A pressurized aircraft cabin is a very different environment from any workplace on land. Aircraft cabin pressure tends to be the equivalent of around 2,300 metres altitude, or a pressure of around 750–780 millibars. This is only about three-quarters of ground-level pressure.

Humidity is much lower than normal workplaces; cabin air typically contains just 3–5 per cent humidity, compared with 60 per cent in temperate zones at sea level. These differences are crucial, because a dehydrated body is often more vulnerable to the effect of toxins.

Also, the cabin is enclosed; people cannot escape from it during their work breaks mid-flight, as factory and office workers on their lunch break can leave the working environment for a walk around the block or to visit a nearby café. A pilot taking a rest during a long-haul flight is still breathing the same air.

The UK Health and Safety Executive's own guidelines on workplace thresholds for hazardous substances clearly state that they are only valid for atmospheric pressures of between 900 and 1,100 millibars.[15] So when the Cranfield researchers stated that the concentrations they found did not breach health and safety guidelines, they were in fact talking about guidelines which were acknowledged not to be relevant to the aircraft environment.

In 2005 the Countess of Mar asked the government, 'What exposure standards currently apply to any synergistic effects of simultaneous exposure to numerous chemicals which may be experienced by aircraft passengers and crew during a contaminated air event in a reduced pressure environment?' The answer, courtesy of Lord Davies of Oldham, was 'None.'[16]

Positive findings

While the Muir report failed to note in its conclusion the high percentages of contaminants detected, analysis of the report by Dr Susan Michaelis and Judith Anderson shows a more worrying reality:

> the report illustrates that the authors identified detectable airborne TOCP [triorthocresyl phosphate] on 14 of the 100 flights, detectable airborne TCPs [tricresyl phosphate] (multiple isomers) on 23 of the 100 flights, and detectable airborne TBPs [tributyl phosphate] on 73 of the 100 flights.[17]

The Cranfield authors did concede that:

> The highest level of TBP recorded was 21.8 μg m^{-3} [micro-

grams per cubic metre] (overall mean 1.07 μg m^{-3}) which exceeds any reported domestic indoor air level. TBP levels were highest during first engine start.[18]

Frank Taylor, visiting fellow in aviation safety at Cranfield University, has complained repeatedly to the government that ministers have misrepresented the Muir team's study. The findings, far from being benign, confirm that there are serious concerns about the safety of cabin air, especially as it is not known whether there are any safe lower limits for exposure to organophosphates. In 2012 he wrote to Lord Attlee, a government spokesman and sponsor of the Civil Aviation Bill, later the Civil Aviation Act 2012. Frank has kindly given me permission to reproduce this excerpt from his letter:

> Some have suggested that the Cranfield report has certain shortcomings but be that as it may the problem as I see it is that the DfT [UK Department for Transport] has claimed, quite incorrectly, that the Cranfield report supports the contention, even proves it, that organophosphates from engine oils present no problem to crew and passengers. The report just does not say this nor even suggest it. ... All that any of us who have dedicated our careers to aviation safety ask is that those with the responsibility and power to take action to prevent future accidents keep an open mind, refrain from making hasty judgements and, difficult though this may be, take time to read crucial evidence for themselves so as to make their own judgement. None of us takes any satisfaction from saying, after an accident, 'I told you so', we all aim to learn from past experience so as to prevent accidents but we can't do this alone.[19]

Dissenters and critics at Cranfield

Frank Taylor has been extremely unhappy with the evasive replies that he has received to this letter and to his other enquiries, both from the government and from the hierarchy at Cranfield. In November 2013 he wrote to Cranfield's vice-chancellor, Professor Sir John O'Reilly, that:

> the [Cranfield Cabin Air] report's conclusion *'With respect*

> *to the conditions of flight that were experienced during this study, there was no evidence for target pollutants occurring in the cabin air at levels exceeding available health and safety standards and guidelines'* does not mean that the higher levels expected during a fume event would also be below such standards.[20]

He added:

> It is also relevant that the report contained no useful discussion about these health and safety standards and guidelines and whether or not they are up to date and, in particular, appropriate for aircraft flight crew. You will be aware that the level of safety set for transport aircraft design and operation is orders of magnitude higher than that acceptable for the general population in other areas. It was therefore extremely surprising to see, soon after the publication of this report, the totally unjustified DfT statement that the Cranfield study had shown that there was no problem associated with contaminated air. To my mind the authors of the Cranfield report should have stepped in at that stage and issued a true account of what could and what could not be inferred from their report but, so far as I am aware, they did not.

The university has not, to the best of my knowledge, distanced itself from misleading ministerial statements that cite the research, but it did distance itself from the dissenting views aired on its own campus at the workshop I mentioned earlier (the one held on 11 October 2011). There was a richly informed, deep discussion on the subject, and a number of important papers gave attendees information on, for example, the known effects on the human nervous system of different chemicals in engine oil, and how these have been known since the 1950s. The workshop papers were subsequently published in a dedicated issue of the *Journal of Biological Physics and Chemistry.*[21]

Dr Graham Holt gave the following impressions of the workshop:

> In 40 years of attending conferences of a scientific nature around the world, I have never encountered a workshop/

> conference such as the one I attended at Cranfield University on 11 October this year [2011]. ...
>
> However, I was unprepared for what followed. I had assumed that the Workshop would answer these questions and that I would be reassured that air travel as a passenger was safe. As the day progressed my comfort zone was severely shaken as the conference provided an eclectic mix of scientific papers and emotional personal diaries of pilots and passengers affected by air travel. The mix of professional science reporting followed almost immediately by evocative and emotional personal stories and some individuals' fights against the system evoked a seesaw of emotions ranging from logical objectivity, empathy and compassion to pride and hope that individuals can fight and win against 'big brother' society. ...
>
> During the day there was considerable humour and the level of sustained interest of the 50 or 60 people present until late at night was quite extraordinary.[22]

After the workshop the university made the highly unusual move of delivering a public rebuke to Professor Ramsden (the Cranfield academic who helped organize the workshop), criticizing the points made at the meeting and in the subsequent publications. The public statement, dated 15 November 2011, which was available on the university website until around October 2013, said for example that:

> Professor Ramsden's contributions on this subject are in an individual capacity and his views do not represent those of Cranfield University. He is not a member of our Institute of Environment and Health (IEH) and is not one of the experts who were involved in the study.[23]

Although the official statement accused Professor Ramsden of quoting selectively from the Muir research report, it did not specifically rebut any of the points he and others made.

My researcher has spoken with Professor Ramsden (who has since left the university).[24] He had a number of points to make regarding the university's statement. I believe it is important to publicize these points, since in my view they are examples of the way in which the debate on these issues is being stifled and distorted.

First, he disputes the implication in the statement that the university had an agreed 'position' on the safety or otherwise of aircraft cabin air, from which he should be seen as a dissenter. The constitutionally correct procedure to establish an official line on any issue is through debate at a meeting of the university's Senate, of which Professor Ramsden was a member at the time. Professor Ramsden did submit a paper on the subject for discussion at Senate, but it was not admitted to the agenda (which is decided by the Vice-Chancellor in his capacity as chairman of the Senate), and no such discussion took place. Academics have a statutory right to present dissenting views, and a professional obligation to conduct research and discussion in a spirit of open-mindedness.

I appreciate that it can be embarrassing to a university if its academics disagree with each other about prominent issues, but to try to stifle debate is contrary to the basic principle of freedom of thought and speech which is fundamental to academic research. I certainly would not accept that it is desirable for any university to establish a settled 'line' on a controversial issue.

Professor Ramsden was understandably unhappy too with the suggestion that the workshop he convened was somehow less 'official' than the Muir research, and that he had put forward his views in a purely personal capacity. From his perspective, he chaired the workshop in his capacity as an officer of the university. Swiss-based Collegium Basilea's role was merely administrative; following Christine Standing's identification of likely participants and masterly organization of the workshop, Professor Ramsden issued the formal invitations, and considers that according to the statutes of the university the event can be counted as an official Cranfield initiative.

Private meetings that Professor Ramsden held with Cranfield colleagues (at which he took notes) give a sense of what was behind this. At his meeting on 9 November 2011 with Professor Tom Stephenson (a self-styled 'executive') of the university, he was told that enquiries about the October workshop had been made to the university's press office, and that the workshop had upset academic colleagues – which he took to mean the authors of the Muir report. They had been invited to the workshop but had not attended, and it was suggested by Tom Stephenson that the purpose of the workshop was to put forward a dissenting position and effectively criticize them. The university saw this as damaging, and Professor Stephenson also referred to 'very upset clients ringing up the university to complain'.

But the point of the workshop was never to take a 'line'; it was designed to explore the issues in a neutral, objective way, and certainly I and other participants believe it did so. As Professor Ramsden put it, 'All we wanted to do was to take an honest view of the evidence.'

Frank Taylor, who also attended on 11 October, and found it 'an extremely interesting and informative day', formally protested about the disparaging comments about the event in the university's press announcement on 15 November.[25]

Probably no one in the whole United Kingdom is more knowledgeable on aviation safety than Frank Taylor. He set up the Cranfield Aviation Safety Centre in 1989, and has led major investigations into air accidents. Aviation safety has been his major reason for intervening in this debate, but a secondary one was the reputation of Cranfield University. He was seriously concerned that the university was liable to damage itself by effectively setting a 'line' on air cabin safety which seemed to derive not so much from the Muir report itself as from the onwards reporting of its findings. As the full truth about toxins in cabin air becomes more widely known, the reputation of this report can only, I believe, fall further.

Note too the comment above about 'clients'. This is not a comment about students, of course; it refers, to the best of my knowledge, to the university's sponsors.

Cranfield University receives tens of millions of pounds of sponsorship money from the aviation industry (including Boeing, Airbus and Rolls-Royce) for projects, research and the like. It boasts of its strategic commercial partners on its website. It also receives funding from the government, such as the funding for the Muir team's research. In these circumstances, it is essential to be wary of any developments which might compromise its independence. I am not accusing the researchers in any way here; whatever reservations others had about the design of the research, there is no reason to doubt that the results (which were by no means universally friendly to the aviation industry, as we have seen) were reported fairly and honestly. But it does seem to me that these subsequent events raise serious questions about the influence of commercial sponsors.

The points made in this chapter were put to Cranfield University in the form of a series of questions, as part of research for this book. In reply, its press office wrote:

> We have reviewed them [your questions], and thank you for the opportunity to reply, but the university has nothing to add to our previous statement issued in November 2011. Cranfield University's Institute of Environment and Health (IEH) undertook a study for the Department for Transport (DfT) in 2008, to investigate aspects of Cabin Air Quality. This work was reported in May 2011. The university is satisfied that the work, findings and conclusions presented in its IEH report are appropriate to the study undertaken. The report is in the public domain and can be viewed at: https://dspace.lib.cranfield.ac.uk/handle/1826/5306.[26]

34

A safe limit?

One point that emerges from the Cranfield research concerns the philosophy surrounding 'safe limits' for organophosphates.

It is standard practice for governments to set down limits for allowable exposure to chemical substances, rather than to ban any exposure whatsoever. The reason is simple: we are all exposed to some degree.

But these limits are a practical issue, and it is misleading to call them 'safe' limits. Quite simply, there is no evidence that exposure to acknowledged toxins is 'safe' at any level. These are limits that have been selected with a view to the scientific evidence, but ultimately in a pragmatic and fairly arbitrary way as those that will be regarded as allowable.

Most chemicals do not have a 'safe limit' designated, and where there is one, it applies to single substances, not mixtures. It will not apply to airline passengers or even 'all' workers, and a limit specified for exposure on the ground should not be taken to apply to the cabin environment at altitude.

It is worth noting too the obvious point that the health impact from a single brief exposure to a toxin is not the same as that from exposure over months and years. For those substances that can accumulate in the body, the low-level exposure, if it continues long enough, can ultimately breach any genuine limit of safety that might exist, and cause significant health problems.

There is serious scientific opinion that there may be no safe limit at all for organophosphates, and that prolonged trace exposures to even very small amounts may be dangerous. This is because of their 'lipophilic' nature – the tendency to attach themselves to human fat and accumulate. A meta-analysis by members of University College London and the UK Open University, published in 2012,[1] showed impaired cognitive ability resulting from damage to the brain and nervous system, which was clearly associated with low-level exposure to organophosphates. It reported that farmers, Gulf War veterans and airline crew were among the groups affected.

Dr Michaelis in her PhD thesis recognized the importance of what is termed the 'synergistic effect':

> The 'Synergistic Effect' of exposure to multiple compounds needs to be considered. Sometimes the combined effect of multiple exposures is considerably greater than the sum of the effects from the individual components. This phenomenon can be one of synergism or potentiation. Synergism occurs when both chemicals have an effect individually and a more than additive effect when together.

Dr Michaelis went on to state that:

> A combination of factors must be considered in flight, which can modify the intensity and effects produced by a noxious substance. Concentrations of contaminants in the cabin air that would not be of significance at sea level may become a hazard at altitude.[2]

35

Scripts and framing

It is extremely difficult to understand the scientific process without taking account of the way in which people understand issues, including how we interpret research findings. As human beings we generally understand issues through a narrative; and in practice the human mind finds it difficult to view its surroundings through more than a small number of 'scripts'. We prioritize some studies above others, and filter out findings that are inconvenient to our dominant narratives.

'Script' as used here is a term that helps to explain how we make sense of the world around us. We use scripts in contexts both trivial and everyday – like wondering why the bus is late – and complex and theoretical – the quantum physicist developing string theory is doing the same thing. We have scripts about men, women, parents, lovers, the government, corporations, trade unions, different nations or nationalities; how they are and how they should be. Sometimes they are crude stereotypes; sometimes they are broadly correct, sometimes wildly inaccurate. But these stories, these presumptions and concepts, are buzzing around in our minds all the time.

Some scripts become dominant, sometimes for reasons that seem trivial, and the script that *'there is no evidence for aerotoxic syndrome'* can easily be seen as one of them. We might also think of this as going along with fashionable thinking, or working within a scientific paradigm. Those who use these dominant narratives believe strongly in them even when in reality the evidence base is patchy or contrary. It gets worse: psychologists have shown that the greater the confidence that is shown in a script, the greater the complacency and the tendency to overlook evidence that could demolish it.

Of course academics learn of these issues, and are trained to be aware of the danger of following a dominant script unthinkingly. These biases are often unconscious, but it is a conscientious researcher's task to make them conscious, to become aware of them and make allowances for them. But even if professional researchers are supposed to be less susceptible to finding what they expect to find than amateurs, it is unlikely that anyone is completely immune.

A related concept with particular relevance in the ongoing debate over the quality of cabin air is 'framing'. Framing refers to the set of assumptions that are made at the outset of any discussion, which determine the space within which it takes place. Framing is inevitable, because we invariably bring with us certain ways of understanding the world, or the issue under discussion, which are often subconscious or cultural in nature. We never come to the table with a blank state of mind. The way in which a subject for discussion is understood and framed shapes the way in which it is discussed. It determines the agenda, with questions such as: Which matters should be prioritized? What is the mainstream, established view, and what is the opposing view?

In a hypothetical debate on cabin air quality in aircraft, a strong set of terms of reference could have been established by those who oppose or challenge the argument that pilots and others travelling on aircraft have been poisoned by substances in the cabin air. Their frame might include the following assumptions:

- The practice of using engine bleed air is very well established. This design for aircraft air intake has been the norm for decades. Therefore, questioning this practice is a maverick position to hold.
- As a result, those challenging the practice should prove their case beyond reasonable doubt. It is fair to expect of them an exceptionally high level of evidence.
- Evidence of hundreds of cases of ill-health resulting from fume events is no more significant than a one-off case, if it is not possible to prove beyond any conceivable doubt that any of the cases are caused by toxins in cabin air.

It is important to appreciate that this set of assumptions is arbitrary and subjective. It would be perfectly possible, for example, to frame the debate quite differently:

- There is growing evidence that a sizeable proportion of those who spend time on aircraft, and particularly on a few readily identifiable models of aircraft, come to suffer from similar health problems.

- Since this proportion is way beyond anything that might occur by chance, there must be a reason for these problems.
- Since there is no indication that before their illness, any of these individuals suffered from mental health problems, there is no reason to prioritize this as a possible cause.
- The first step should be to avoid a spread of the problem, by grounding the aircraft that give cause for concern. The second step should be a thorough investigation to see if common elements are present. The third step should then be to apply the obvious solutions (effective filters and monitoring devices, for example).

Do airlines and aircraft manufacturers want the debate to be framed in this way? Of course not. The first kind of framing is convenient for the industry, so their representatives work hard to ensure that it is the dominant script or paradigm.

There is also a growing difference between what companies say and what they do. In public, there is near-universal denial of the problem; behind the scenes, and often kept that way by confidentiality clauses, there is evident acceptance that people are being poisoned, and there are deals made to compensate at least some of them.

'There is no evidence' is a worrying phrase. If there is no evidence, it does not mean that the issue does not exist. It could equally mean that because of the way the debate has been framed, no one has looked for a certain type of evidence. And if you do not look for it, you tend not to find it.

We have seen this even in instances as blatant as the attempt to dissuade individuals from undergoing physical tests, with spurious arguments such as exaggerating their difficulty or expense. If you don't test someone's blood or fat samples to see if there is a raised level of toxins, you won't find the evidence of a raised level.

It is easy for people to conclude, when they keep hearing that 'there is no evidence' relating to the problems that sufferers complain about, that there *is* an evidence base that use of bleed air is safe. But that is not a logical conclusion. It would be practically impossible to produce conclusive evidence of such a thing. At best we could only work with a *hypothesis* that the use of bleed air is safe. And does the evidence we have assembled support such a hypothesis? In my and many others' opinion, it is very clear that it does not.

Coincidences and correlations

A correlation – two things occurring at the same time, or one directly after the other – is not the same as a cause. For example, if there is a pile-up of five cars on the motorway and they are all coloured red, we don't assume that it is the redness that caused the collision. Why don't we do so? Because there are plenty of other possible causes, for example road conditions, visibility, driver tiredness and errors, and the roadworthiness of the cars.

(Even that is not proof that the redness *didn't* contribute to the collision; in fact there is plenty of evidence accumulated over a long time that there *is* some correlation between the colour of cars and their accident rate.[1])

Unlikely correlations occurring once, or at most only a handful of times, tend to be dismissed. But even unlikely correlations that occur repeatedly deserve further investigation.

So it is specious when spokespeople (especially spokespeople for interested organizations) play the 'coincidence card' too often and too readily. Here's another example. A report by the European Aviation Safety Agency (EASA) was also cited by the Australian Expert Panel:

> A causal relationship between the reported health symptoms and oil/hydraulic fluid contamination has not been established. As there is no conclusive scientific evidence available, the Agency is not able to justify a rule-making task to change the existing design or certification specifications.[2]

You might think that if all the cases mentioned in this book – and countless other well-documented cases – of individuals breathing in toxic fumes and then feeling ill does not constitute sufficient evidence, then what could possibly do so?

The aviation industry and, alas, regulators such as the EASA, tend to argue that cases of pilot/cabin crew/passenger ill-health should be taken one by one, and that if a single case cannot be proved to be caused by fumes, then that is all that can be said. It's not. While it is necessary to caution against over-interpreting a correlation, it is equally important to acknowledge the significance of strong correlations, especially when we are dealing with safety and human health. If a disproportionate number of travellers on a certain type of aircraft are taken ill over a considerable period of time – and all with the same symptoms – then that *does* constitute evidence of something that warrants further investigation.

David Michaels, a health and safety expert, and currently President Obama's Assistant Secretary for Labor at the US Occupational Safety & Health Administration, has studied the tactics that corporations or indeed entire industry sectors use to defend unethical or otherwise questionable practices. They do this by sowing just sufficient uncertainty into the public debate. My colleague Tristan Loraine drew my attention to David's article 'Doubt is their product', published in *Scientific American* in 2005. In it he wrote:

> Uncertainty is an inherent problem of science, but manufactured uncertainty is another matter entirely. Over the past three decades, industry groups have frequently become involved in the investigative process when their interests are threatened. If, for example, studies show that a company is exposing its workers to dangerous levels of a certain chemical, the business typically responds by hiring its own researchers to cast doubt on the studies. Or if a pharmaceutical firm faces questions about the safety of one of its drugs, its executives trumpet company-sponsored trials that show no significant health risks while ignoring or hiding other studies that are much less reassuring. The vilification of threatening research as 'junk science' and the corresponding sanctification of industry-commissioned research as 'sound science' has become nothing less than standard operating procedure in some parts of corporate America.[3]

The result is that those challenging the accepted version of events are forced to cross an almost infinitely high threshold of evidence before their research can be taken seriously – while little or no evidence is required for the industry's view.

It is notable that representatives for the aviation industry and public bodies minded to support it never directly challenge the evidence patiently assembled by eminent scientists such as Professor Mohamed Abou-Donia, Professor Clement Furlong, Professor Chris Winder, Dr Jonathan Burdon and the many others who have convincingly demonstrated the link between contaminated aircraft cabin air and serious consequent ill-health. Rather, they cite other studies, often selectively, and publish these messages prominently while refusing to acknowledge the existence of others. This creates just enough doubt to keep the issue a little way short of settled in the public mind. It's called *kicking the can down the road*, and they imagine that we don't see what they're doing. Or perhaps they calculate or hope that not enough of us do so.

Here is an example of a conclusion from one of the many inquiries into toxic cabin air. Superficially it appears cautious and scientific, but analysis shows how it understates the inherent risks with a disingenuous line of reasoning. This is from the report on the 2000 inquiry by the UK House of Lords:

> The absence of confirmed cases of tri-ortho-cresyl phosphate (TOCP) poisoning from cabin air and the very low levels of TOCP that would be found in even the highly unlikely worst case of contamination from oil leaking into the air supply lead us to conclude that the concerns about significant risk to the health of airline passengers and crew are not substantiated.[4]

What is wrong with this? Let me point out some of the ways in which it distorts the issues.

- The tri-ortho isomer of tricresyl phosphate is not the most toxic of the isomers in jet engine oil, and is likely to be barely present at all.
- There is no mention at all of other isomers of TCP which dominate the TCP blends in engine oil formulations. Their toxic nature is less well established by pertinent information has been in the public domain since at least 1958.
- The phrase 'absence of confirmed cases' skirts all the issues of complexity in identifying the causes of illness. 'Confirmed' is a particularly objectionable weasel word; what rates as a

confirmed case? What about all the cases of sickness which were never examined as possible TOCP (or other isomer) poisoning?

- 'Highly unlikely worst case' is just rubbish. Fume events are not highly unlikely at all. They occur frequently, if not daily, and there is at least some presence of these toxic chemicals in cabin air whenever the aircraft engines are running, as we have seen. This statement deftly implies that fume events are no more than hypothetical. They are not. As well as many cases that have not been documented, there are many, many documented fume events.

Overall, a wholly misleading picture is created through careful arrangement of individual phrases that are mostly not quite untrue individually. Selective omission and the conscious sowing of doubt are used to leave the bigger and more deadly picture hidden.

36

Holidays to Hell

Samantha Sabatino's story

Samantha Sabatino and her family of four had been passengers on a flight from the United Kingdom to Florida on 1 February 2007 when they experienced a fume event. This led to severe respiratory problems for all the family, who until then had enjoyed excellent health, as well as for other passengers. Samantha and her family spent their entire holiday in hospital, being treated for acute smoke inhalation.

The following is an excerpt from the Stewarts Law Attorney Group summary of the claim brought by 20 British passengers – including Samantha Sabatino's family – against XL Airways:

> The Stewarts Law Attorney Group represents 20 British passengers who were seriously injured by aircraft toxic fumes exposure on 1 February 2007. The incident occurred when they were flying on board an XL Airways Boeing 767 from London Gatwick to Sanford International, Florida.
>
> The dangerous toxins were released into the cabin through the bleed air system which (as on most airliners) draws high pressure air from the core of the engines to pressurise the aircraft with breathable air. It has long been known that this design can result in the cabin air becoming contaminated with toxic oil vapour when the engine oil seals leak.
>
> The toxins were detected by passengers as they began to notice an odd smell similar to 'smelly socks'. The cabin seemed more 'stuffy' and 'hot' than any previous flight they had been on and the air severely irritated their eyes, nose and throat. The passengers quickly became ill, suffering respiratory symptoms, severe headaches, vomiting, bowel problems, skin blistering and extreme fatigue. The toxic air has also caused long term chronic effects such as respiratory problems, memory loss, sleep disturbance, chronic fatigue, mood swings, cognitive difficulties, infections, and joint/limb pains.

> In order to put pressure on the US manufacturers to deal with these known cabin air problems and to obtain fair compensation for the passengers, on 29 January 2009 specialist litigation firm Stewarts Law filed the case in Illinois, the state where Boeing has its Headquarters. In addition to Boeing, the case was filed against Hamilton Sundstrand (which manufactures air system components), United Technologies (which manufactures the Pratt & Whitney engines) and the owners of the aircraft – AAR Parts Trading Inc.
>
> This is an outright US product liability case against US defendants. However, the defendants were intent on having the case sent back to the UK courts (which are much more expensive for claimants and award much lower compensation) so they filed a forum non conveniens motion arguing that the UK is the most convenient place for the litigation.
>
> After prolonged legal battle, on 3 May 2010 Judge Quinn decided in favour of the passengers and dismissed the defendants' forum non conveniens motion. Stewarts Law has achieved a great victory for the passengers. Securing US jurisdiction along with the prospect of a high profile jury trial is a wake up call for US manufacturers – unless they take measures to improve the quality of cabin air now, they will face the credible prospect of expensive and public US litigation for future incidents where there is an identifiable toxic fumes leak that causes injury.[1]

Samantha told me about the response from the airline and manufacturer when she complained. The airline Excel told her 'You are the only passenger to complain' which she knew was not true. She had been in contact with about forty passengers who had all filed complaints. When she contacted Boeing, she talked first to someone who took her for an airline staff member. She was told that 'If you have a bleed air valve failure, you are going to have bad health due to toxic fumes.' When she explained that she was actually a passenger, the line went dead.

Samantha and her family's experience was featured in the 2008 BBC *Panorama* programme and more recently in the Australian *60 Minutes* show.

The Isherwood family's story

Karen Isherwood and her family were passengers travelling with Ryanair to Tenerife at the end of July 2011 for a two-week family holiday. Karen had a history of chest infections – she had had pneumonia twice and suffered regular occurrences of pleurisy – but she was otherwise fit and well. She was studying for an MBA and working on setting up her own business, in coaching and consultancy.

On the flight Karen and her family didn't smell anything especially unusual. Her family were sat about six or eight rows from the front of the plane.

Although she felt fine during the flight, immediately after it Karen began to feel woozy and unwell. She thought this was perhaps her reaction to the change of temperature between England and Tenerife. But her symptoms didn't wear off, instead they intensified. The next day, she says, 'I was having electric shocks on the right side of my temple which made me feel terrible, I was still in and out of a woozy state and having a racing heartbeat, sickly stomach and completely fatigued. I had tremors in my hands and feet. I had a continuous migraine with pain in my face and eye sockets.' She saw a doctor, who told her she was having brain seizures, and advised her to go to hospital if she felt no better after a couple of days. As her condition did not improve, Karen did so, and after a full series of tests the doctors at the hospital diagnosed peripheral vertigo, chronic sinusitis and migraine. The treatment she was prescribed made her no better, and she continued to be seriously unwell after the holiday ended.

Karen felt sure her illness was related to the flight, because it had started so quickly after it, and she used her professional skills as a researcher to see if she could find out about 'illness following a flight'. This brought her in contact with fellow sufferers, and with my own Aerotoxic Association. She has no doubt that she is suffering from aerotoxic syndrome – no other explanation matched her symptoms – but the doctors she consulted did not take this seriously as an alternative.

> I did see a neurologist who told me I was suffering with migraines. I didn't believe it, as he couldn't explain any other symptoms. ... Another consultant ... advised me to

> take Prozac for depression as he thought I had suffered a breakdown because of stress. ... I was advised to see the chronic fatigue syndrome team who diagnosed me with having this at a very high level because of my personality type.
>
> I did not finish my MBA, I did not start the business, I didn't feel like me any more.[2]

Karen's local MP, Andy Burnham – a personal acquaintance – wrote to the Department of Transport in February 2012, and shortly afterwards she got a letter from Theresa Villiers MP, then the UK Transport Minister. It told her that although there had been a number of reported incidents around the world, the conclusion of research – reference was made particularly to the Cranfield University study – was that there was '*no evidence of pollutants occurring in cabin air at levels exceeding available health and safety standards and guidelines*'. Ms Villiers added that '*There is no accepted medical condition called aerotoxic syndrome.*' This was despite her calling for a full public enquiry into cabin air quality when she was a Conservative party spokesperson (in a 2008 press release).[3]

It is understandable that airlines resist diagnoses of aerotoxic syndrome, because any admission that people's problems are related to fume exposure in aircraft would make them legally and financially liable. But why should some university researchers and politicians refuse to acknowledge what the sufferers themselves are sure is the correct diagnosis, because there is no plausible alternative, by not just denying that individuals have aerotoxic syndrome, but denying that such a syndrome exists? That is something we need to investigate further.

37

What happens in court?

When there is, according to numerous industry and ministerial statements, 'no evidence' to support a diagnosis of aerotoxic syndrome, it is remarkable just how often, when sufferers make a legal claim, they manage to win compensation. Often these cases don't go to court; the airline or aircraft manufacturer makes an out-of-court settlement. Of course, this avoids any formal legal precedent being set, and ensures that publicity is minimized. That's unfortunate for those of us campaigning to see the issue recognized more widely, although it's understandable for the individuals who choose to settle. Let's look now at some of those who have taken the aviation industry to court.

Judy Cullinane v Ansett Airlines

In 2002 Judy Cullinane, a former flight attendant at Australian-based carrier Ansett Airlines, won an out-of-court settlement for ill-health resulting from fume events on the BAe 146 aircraft on which she worked. Other claimants also received compensation, but Ms Cullinane was the first to obtain hers in settlement of a lawsuit.[1]

The claim was based on a lack of proper sealing on the BAe 146's air conditioning system, which had allowed engine fumes to enter the cabin. Ms Cullinane suffered symptoms which we have seen are typical of aerotoxic syndrome: long-term headaches, nausea, hair loss and lethargy. She took a period of sick leave but found herself unable to resume work afterwards.

Ms Cullinane's solicitor, Hayden Stephens of Slater and Gordon, told the media, 'Fortunately Ms Cullinane will be properly compensated for lost income and medical expenses for injuries she suffered through no fault of her own.' Ms Cullinane herself said in the documentary *Welcome Aboard Toxic Airlines*, 'They never told the truth to the crew or passengers. They don't want those documents out in the public arena.'[2]

Flight attendants v Alaska Airlines

In January 2003, Alaska Airlines paid $725,000 to settle a lawsuit by twenty-six flight attendants who reported having been made ill by toxic leaks into aircraft. According to the *Seattle Times*, under a confidentiality agreement the attendants signed a statement acknowledging that the airline had never intended to harm them and had since taken measures to improve workplace safety.[3]

The *Times* reported that the deal gave $4,068 to each attendant, making a total of $105,768; $6,000 to be divided among the attendants to cover medical expenses; and about $292,000 for legal fees and expenses to be divided among lawyers and the flight attendants' union. The rest of the settlement, more than $320,000, was designated for financing litigation against the other defendants (presumably the aircraft and/or parts manufacturers).

The lawsuit had been filed in 1998, and followed complaints by more than 900 attendants, who said (according to the press report) that they had experienced 'unexplained headaches, tremors, impaired mental abilities and other sickness aboard flights during the previous 10 years'.

The *Times* reported that some Alaska Airlines mechanics said that hydraulic fluid and lubricating oil got sucked into the cabin ventilation systems from leaks in the APU. At the time, Alaska Airlines officials admitted that hydraulic leaks had caused 'temporary' illnesses, but maintained that it had taken extensive and costly measures to reduce leaks.

Joanne Turner v East-West Airlines

Joanne Turner's fight for justice took nearly two decades. A flight attendant but flying as a passenger with the Australian company East-West Airlines, she suffered a fume event on a flight from Sydney to Brisbane in 1992. A cracked compressor carbon seal on the BAe 146 caused 'dust and fumes' to leak into the cabin air. Joanne was twenty-five weeks pregnant at the time. As the eventual Australian High Court judgement stated:

> As the aircraft was descending into Brisbane, for a period of about 20 minutes, smoke was emitted into the cabin. There was a thick cloud of smoke. The immediate effect of that smoke upon the respondent included coughing, a burning throat, sore eyes and a headache. Thereafter the respondent suffered from a persistent cough. On occasions the cough worsened, particularly when the respondent had a cold.[4]

These symptoms were unpleasant, but Joanne recovered sufficiently to continue working for the next ten years. However she continued to experience ill-health, and in particular respiratory problems, and in 2001 she took the airline to the New South Wales Dust Diseases Tribunal in a bid for compensation.

The airline was judged to have been negligent, and was ordered to pay her $139,000. It appealed against the judgement, however, and the case went as far as the Supreme Court of New South Wales. Its full judgement, published on 1 April 2010, should be required reading for the legal departments and risk managers of every airline in the world. The company by then was no longer trading, so it was doubtful whether Ms Turner would ever get her compensation, although she made it clear that the money was not her motivation. 'I just hope it will help fellow crew members who also have cases before the courts and help the industry become safer', she said.

On appeal, the case then went to the High Court of Australia on 3 September 2010, and historically was the first case of its sort to be won.

Tanya Segelov, Joanne's lawyer, added, 'This will provide a significant global precedent for thousands of pilots, cabin crew and passengers who may have been exposed to similar toxic fumes on these aircraft which were operated worldwide.'[5]

Terry Williams v Boeing

One of the most significant cases of recent years was settled by a manufacturer, Boeing, not an airline, in Washington state, USA in October 2011. Former cabin crew member Terry Williams was awarded unspecified damages in what was once again a confidential out-of-court settlement.[6] This case is particularly important because Ms Williams' case was apparently based on the fundamental design weakness of using bleed air, rather than simply being attributed to a one-off case of poor maintenance by an airline. Boeing, to its enormous credit, is doing far more than other manufacturers to prevent future problems, by moving to the modern bleed-free system with its B787.

Willem Felderhof v KLM

Legal action was continuing in this case at the time of writing, and it was looking more like a score-draw than a win for either side, but again it set important precedents.[7] Willem Felderhof is a pilot who was forced to retire early through ill-health which he was convinced had been triggered by repeated fume leaks. Because 'aerotoxic syndrome' was not at the time accepted as a medical condition by law courts or the insurance industry in the Netherlands, he sought to have it recognized as an occupational illness, in part to qualify for insurance-related payments.

In September 2013 the court ordered KLM to carry out tests on air quality on its entire fleet of Boeing 737s – eighty-three aircraft in total. It set a tight deadline, and required an independent institute to carry out the tests. In mid-December the results came back: all the aircraft had tested positive for tricresyl phosphate.

TNO, a Dutch scientific research institute, found TCP in ten Boeing 737 aircraft that were tested out of a total of forty-six of the KLM fleet. Thirty-seven out of eighty air samples showed TCP, which is close to 50 per cent. The peak concentration was 155 ng/m^3. It was proudly stated, four times, that 'No ToCP was found', which is to be expected given the regulations that disallow anything but very low (and preferably zero) TOCP content in the TCP blends added to these aviation oils!

When approached for comment, Professor van Netten (who we shall meet again in Chapter 40) stated:

- The chromosorb 106 tubes (used to sample the cabin air) are meant for active vapour measurements and not for aerosols.

- TCP isomers do not have enough vapour pressure at room temperature to be measured.
- Therefore, TCP isomers in the aircraft air are found as an aerosol, most likely condensed onto dust particles.
- The chromosorb SKC 106 tubes are not designed to capture aerosols, hence the poor results from TNO.

Wipe samples were taken with demineralized water. It is like removing olive oil from a surface with a wet tissue; most of it remains on the table. Consequently reported highest values were very low.[8]

KLM presented these results as a victory, claiming that the amounts were too small to have caused Captain Felderhof's injuries, but it is significant that this dangerous contaminant was found at all, and there is certainly cause to question this claim. Note that as in the Cranfield study, this did not involve an analysis of a fume event, so it was evidence of a background level of toxins in aircraft bleed air. Captain Felderhof's union expressed dissatisfaction with KLM's stance, and pledged to continue the case.

Unnamed flight attendant v British Airways

British Airways' insurers have agreed liability in the case of a young flight attendant made seriously ill by fume events aboard Boeing 767s. Settlement on the compensation to be awarded was being finalized at the time of writing.

These are cases of which I am personally aware, but there is no doubt that many people are paid to go quietly, receiving a substantial sum in return for confidentiality agreements which they honour, so their cases do not become more widely known. In other instances, particularly where individuals have suffered severe brain damage, people either do not realize that they have a good case, or they do not feel able to accept the stress of pursuing it. We hear of many unreported or new cases at the office of the Aerotoxic Association every week. Much more evidence of individual sufferers is available in our archives.

The Richard Westgate case

Since the formation of the Aerotoxic Association I have been contacted by countless aircrew and passengers, all of whom seek advice or an explanation for their mysterious symptoms. I am frequently asked how many people have contacted the Aerotoxic Association since 2007. On 19 April 2013 I wrote a personal letter to aviation minister Lord Attlee to make him aware that since the Association's foundation I had received approximately 250 separate testimonies from aircrew and passengers whose health had been adversely affected by exposure to toxic oil fumes. The testimonies included four common themes: initial good health which becomes serious chronic mysterious ill health; a causal link between toxic oil fumes and symptoms consistent with exposure; state registered doctors still being unfamiliar with diagnosis and treatment and individuals wishing to be tested to prove exposure and recover their health. My letter was ignored.[9]

As my administration skills are poor and I had no day-to-day assistance from 2007 until late 2013, it has been impossible to keep track of the actual number or the fate of international contacts, so I use the term 'countless', when asked 'how many people?' Richard Westgate made contact with the Association on 16 March 2012, and was one of the pilots whose evidence I included in my letter.

Richard was a senior first officer with BA and a pilot of sixteen years flying experience; he was slim, fit and a paragliding champion. In his email to me he asked: 'Do you have any doctors you recommend for treatment as I am deteriorating badly and my doc hasn't got a clue?'[10] As with many others, I referred him to my good friend Dr Michel Mulder and his team of medical specialists for possible treatment in the Netherlands.

Although the Aerotoxic Association was Richard Westgate's first contact with the issue, I never actually met Richard as he single-mindedly went straight to the Netherlands for urgent treatment from Dr Mulder. Later we exchanged emails and spoke extensively on Skype in 2012. Richard became passionate about alerting the medical community to this little known cause of ill-health, and we were all deeply shocked when he suddenly died at the age of 43 on 12 December 2012.

Richard Westgate, who died on 12 December 2012

I was able to meet Richard's friends and family in Dorset at his moving humanist funeral on a snowy day in January 2013, and in May the Westgate family held a memorial flying weekend, where I found out from his many friends that he had been in poor health for years. Like the rest of us, Richard had been grossly misdiagnosed and mistreated with antidepressants, but it was clear that the Westgate family (including his twin brother and fellow pilot Guy) wished to understand the cause of Richard's death. Anyone who knew him would confirm that it would be difficult to find a less depressed fellow human being, and that treatment with antidepressants would never have worked.

Much time, expense and harm would be saved in the future if doctors listened more carefully to their patients and familiarized themselves with the published scientific findings about organophosphate poisoning, some of which date from the 1950s.[11]

At the time of writing, a UK coroner's court is conducting an investigation into his death, with a view to collecting evidence for the inquest, where the cause of his death should be determined. While Richard's death was tragic, the coroner's case will undoubtedly be significant for three reasons.

The first is that the court will make a declaration about the cause of the death, and the strength of the causal link between the neurological damage consistent with organophosphate poisoning, and the bleed-air system of supplying cabin air. This could be seen as either a direct cause or a 'facilitator' of his death.

Second, if this causal link is accepted, then the coroner may then rule on measures necessary to prevent future deaths from occurring.

Third, a ruling that the poisoning was either the cause of or the facilitator to Richard's death will enable other actions to be taken against the industry by affected aircrew and passengers still living.

Frank Cannon, the lawyer acting for Richard's family commented, 'They can try explaining one [case] away, but not another and then another.'[12]

38

Sample sizes and research agreements

One of the arguments regularly made by those who refuse to recognize an aerotoxic problem is that much of the research that has been done has been on a relatively small scale. The reason for that is simple. Research is expensive, and it is not easy to obtain funding for large-scale research. My colleagues and I all expect to see more research take place. But not surprisingly, there is little or no aviation industry support for research into aerotoxic syndrome, and indeed as we have seen, the industry has on occasion made conscious efforts to frustrate research initiatives. The most memorable of these was the (UK) CAA's refusal in 2006 to assist in a survey of BAe 146 pilots, discussed below.

Susan Michaelis's BAe 146 survey

In 2007, while still in recovery from my illness, I was asked by Susan Michaelis to help conduct this survey. I was tasked with contacting other BAe 146 pilots, asking them standardized personal questions about their health and recording their answers. I found this work difficult, partly because of my own poor condition, and also because it involved asking both strangers and friends for highly personal information. Yet a complete survey was critical to any outside understanding of what was being openly denied by certain medical practitioners.

In spite of the problems, the survey did go ahead, though not without difficulties. The results showed that 44 per cent of the pilots surveyed had suffered short-term ill-health effects, 32 per cent had suffered long-term health effects and 13 per cent had lost their medical certificates as a result of chronic ill-heath.[1]

Susan's survey and its findings were presented in her thesis entitled *Health and Flight Safety Implications from Exposure to*

Contaminated Air in Aircraft, and contributed to the award of her PhD by the University of New South Wales in 2011. I consider this thesis to be a bible on the aerotoxic issue.

I found it hugely frustrating that, after I had recorded my own details and helped interview 273 other pilots, the survey wasn't even acknowledged by the authorities. This sense of frustration was compounded by a feeling of disappointment in University College London and elsewhere, whose staff until recently had taken a keen interest in the health and damage done to professional pilots.

I report some more research results in this chapter, focusing in particular on research that measures the problems found in affected aircrew, and on research that looks for links between the problems they report and other physical markers. This latter kind is particularly important because it refutes so decisively the suggestion that any of these symptoms are psychosomatic. Not only can we link the symptoms very clearly to exposure to toxins, we can also point to non-symptomatic physical changes that accompany them. Most of these studies are indeed based on small samples, but please bear in mind that is not a deliberate choice on the part of the researchers, it is a reflection of the fact that it is very difficult to obtain funding for research in this field, so the researchers have to tailor their research designs to the limited funding that they do receive.

Dr Mackenzie Ross's studies

In Chapter 21 I described research by Dr Sarah Mackenzie Ross in which I participated in 2006. It is true it was based on a small sample (twenty-seven pilots), but that does not alter the fact that the outcomes were very clear: 100 per cent of the pilots were affected in the same way.

In 2011 Dr Mackenzie Ross published findings of a further study, based on a sample from the IPA database.[2] Again she focused on testing pilots' and ex-pilots' intellectual functioning, this time using the Wechsler Adult Intelligence Scale (WAIS)-III. This scale comprises fourteen subsets which measure a variety of verbal and nonverbal functions, working memory and processing speed. Dr Mackenzie Ross also included measures to test a participant's effort, using a medical symptom validity test. This helps ensure a like-for-like comparison. The group of pilots was then compared with a group of individuals exposed to organo-phosphates in pesticides, and both pilots and pesticide-poisoning sufferers were compared with the general population.

A total of twenty-nine pilots were assessed, a random subsample of seventy who had initially completed a questionnaire. Again, this was a small sample, but this was not Dr Mackenzie Ross's choice. She had applied to the UK government for funding for a larger-scale study, but she did not receive it, so she had no alternative but to carry out her research on a small scale.

She found that the pilots and the individuals with pesticide exposure showed similar patterns of cognitive ability and impairment. The pilots scored higher on IQ, which was to be expected considering the educational requirements for these occupations. Both groups consistently showed significant impairment in three areas: tests of attention, psychomotor speed and visual sequencing. This pattern was markedly different from that of the general population. The full results, together with a summary of the 2006 findings, were reported in the *Journal of Biological Physics and Chemistry* in 2011.

Dr Mackenzie Ross pointed out in her paper that the Committee on Toxicity had recommended in 2007 that the UK government carry out a wide-scale epidemiological survey of cabin crew. This has yet to take place.

Professor Abou-Donia's research

Mohamed Abou-Donia of Duke University, NC, USA, who holds professorships in pharmacology, cancer biology and neurobiology, published in 2012 the findings of a study of thirty-four aircrew (pilots and flight attendants) who reported adverse effects after exposure to in-flight emissions.[3] He took serum samples from these individuals, and examined their chemical make-up. He compared their results with those of twelve healthy individuals who acted as controls.

Significant elevations in auto-antibodies consistent with neurological complaints were found in the flight crew, but not in the controls. This is important because it gives us a 'biomarker' for neurological damage. If it is possible to show that the neurological damage is related to a physical change such as an increase in auto-antibodies, this effectively demolishes the argument that the symptoms might be purely psychosomatic.

Professor Abou-Donia also carried out an in-depth case study of a single pilot who had been grounded after showing the symptoms of aerotoxic syndrome.[4] Again, this is particularly interesting because serum samples were taken from the individual before he showed symptoms, after he developed them, and subsequently while he was not flying and was slowly recovering his health.

This pilot had developed clinical problems after flying for forty-five hours over just ten days. He had reported reduced memory capacity, and on one occasion had experienced sudden deafness and vertigo on one side. After being grounded, he suffered nausea, vomiting, nystagmus, loss of equilibrium and inner ear problems.

Professor Abou-Donia noted that 'Significant increases in auto-antibodies were noted to most of the tested proteins in the serum of this pilot after exposure to air emissions.'[5] In other words, this individual did not just show the outward signs of aerotoxic syndrome, it was possible to see internal changes in his body, in the form of the level of auto-antibodies in his serum samples. As his condition grew worse, the levels of auto-antibodies continued to rise. Then when he had not been flying for a year his condition began to improve, and a drop in the auto-antibodies again reflected the disappearance of his symptoms.

The research report emphasized that more information is needed on the chemical composition of emissions in cabin air. It also recommended that infants, the elderly and chronically ill people should be protected either by operating aircraft with a non-bleed air intake system or by filtering the air before circulation in the cabin.

Dr Burdon's research

Dr Jonathan Burdon, from Melbourne, Australia, is a respiratory physician with an interest in occupational lung disorders and a past president of the Thoracic Society of Australia and New Zealand. He became interested in the aerotoxic syndrome when he was approached for help by a pilot suffering from this condition in 1999. Since that time he has been consulted by a significant number of air crew, both nationally and internationally, who have developed symptoms as a result of fume events during the course of their flying duties. As a result his work has been largely related to the clinical aspects of this condition and, for obvious reasons, to those persons with respiratory problems. However, as the inhalation of toxic fumes subsequently leads to their absorption through the lungs and into the bloodstream, he has also had a significant experience with general clinical symptomatology.

He has, with others, published his experience of the presenting symptoms of patients who have become ill after a fume event. He has reported a wide range of symptoms which include breathlessness, cough, wheeze, chronic sinusitis, fatigue, gastro-intestinal symptoms including nausea, difficulties with speech, short-term memory, dizziness, poor concentration and other neuro-cognitive deficits and an acute onset confusional state, just to mention a few. It is also clear, as with other conditions caused by the inhalation of fumes, that there is a differential sensitivity between individuals. Most persons have a recurrence of symptoms when they return to cabin duties, and symptoms have continued after ceasing work in some. Dr Burdon has argued that, while TCP toxicity would explain many of the symptoms seen in this condition, it is likely that as the fumes of pyrolyzed engine oil contain many substances, it is not TCP alone that might causing injury when inhaled. He has also noted that lung injury may be subtle and that routine lung function tests are often unhelpful. He has been a strong advocate against the 'hyperventilation theory' as an explanation for the presenting and long-term complaints of afflicted air crew and other exposed personnel.

The Schindler research

A team headed by B. K. Schindler carried out research which was reported in *Archives of Toxicology* in April 2013.[6] The study was funded by the German Social Accident Insurance Institution, and covered fifty-one flights. This study tested the urine from a relatively large sample of 332 pilots and cabin crew members (in common passenger airliners) who had reported seeing fumes or smelling an odour during their last flight. The analysis looked for three isomers of tricresyl phosphate metabolites as well as dialkyl and diaryl phosphate metabolites of four flame retardants. These samples were compared with samples of unexposed individuals from the general population, and it was found that the median metabolite levels of tributyl phosphate (TBP), tris-(2-chloroethyl) phosphate (TCEP) and triphenyl phosphate (TPP) were significantly higher in the aircrew. The median metabolite levels of tris-(2-chloropropyl) phosphate (TCPP) were not significantly higher in the aircrews than in the controls. However, as with all the other on-board studies of which I am aware, none of the sample of fifty-one flights suffered a recorded fume event.

Again, this offers sound scientific evidence that aircrew do absorb toxic chemicals even when a fume event is not recorded.[7]

Dr Hageman finds neurological symptoms

Dr Hageman, of Medisch Spectrum, Twente, the Netherlands, is a neurologist. He examined thirty pilots who reported symptoms following exposure to fumes in aircraft cabins, and reported:

> They feel decidedly unwell. They have difficulty with their vision – it's hard for them to adjust their focusing between near and far. From far to near is particularly difficult. Some of them suffer from headaches and migraines, which must make it hard for them to fly a plane.[8]

He added that a pilot often becomes badly affected, and has to ask the co-pilot to take over. Pilots have told him that they continue flying, even though they have problems concentrating and have nearly fainted in the cockpit. 'We've seen so many people here over the years who were so ill they were unable to work, as a result of really serious symptoms. This cannot be ignored.'

Dr Julu's research

Dr Peter Julu at the Breakspear Medical Group in the southern United Kingdom has examined sixteen pilots, and found links between reports of fume events and a consistent pattern of serious neurological damage in all the pilots he has seen. He found that:

> The pilots were experiencing neurological symptoms such as memory loss, tremors, lethargy and poor cognitive functions. These were associated with and reinforced by other non-specific symptoms of aerotoxic syndrome, for example, flu-like illnesses that do not go away.[9]

Dr Julu conducted what he calls 'target-organ oriented examination of the autonomic nervous system', which he believes can give firm evidence of nerve damage caused by chemical contamination and other neurotoxins.

These outline findings are significant enough. What is even more striking is that Dr Julu found the same pattern of neurological disturbance in airline pilots as is present in farmers known to have suffered organophosphate poisoning – without knowing that there were any organophosphates in the aircraft environment. Initially, he found the unusual pattern of injuries to be a puzzle.

Dr Julu is a specialist in autonomic neurophysiology. This relates to those functions of the brain that the conscious mind does not directly control, such as the heartbeat. Those that the mind does control, such as walking and hand movements, are known as somatic. Breathing lies uniquely in both categories.

Neurologists and other doctors often refer patients to Dr Julu when there is evidence of impairment to the autonomic features. A few years ago, he started receiving referrals of airline pilots. In an interview for this book, he explained what he discovered:

> The reason why pilots started coming to me was that a neurologist would note that some parts of the autonomic nervous system were not working, and asked me to confirm.
>
> What I do is, as the system controls all the organs, I look at the pattern of abnormalities: the parts of the brain that are working well, the parts that are not working well; some parts may be doing this, the lungs doing something else; the blood pressure may be behaving like this. There are so many

different types, that it is difficult for you to establish one abnormality only and come up with a diagnosis – it's better to look for negative, positive patterns, like a barcode. So, I know what Diabetes II looks like, Parkinsons, and so on.

The pattern of autonomic disturbance in pilots was not tying in with any of the abnormalities that I was familiar with – they were a class of their own. Luckily enough, at that time DEFRA [the UK agriculture ministry] had commissioned me to look at farmers, because they were also suspecting that there was something the matter with them owing to the sheep dipping. With the farmers, they knew that they were exposed to something environmentally toxic, organophosphates. By law they had to dip their animals. The government knew about that.

The strange thing was, what I presented to BALPA was the fact that the pattern of autonomic disturbances in the farmers was similar to those in the pilots. That was the strange thing. Of course, there were a lot of arguments from the airline industry saying it could be carbon monoxide poisoning. They were not denying there was something the matter, something in the cockpit. But what they were saying was that it must be carbon monoxide. They were sorting that one out because they were already installing CO detectors in the planes.

Also, some miners were trapped in a mine in south Yorkshire, with a failed vent; they were taking a legal case. Their lawyer contacted me. They settled out of court. For them it was proven that they were poisoned with CO; no question, the authorities didn't deny that. The pattern was different to that for the pilots. I presented that to BALPA: 'I have the pattern for CO, and it is different from the pilots – theirs is similar to organophosphate poisoning.'

Of course there are organophosphates in jet engine oil, but at that time Dr Julu did not know that. He added:

An aeronautical engineer wrote to me from Israel – it was a very long letter – that there are organophosphates in quite a few aviation products: jet engine oil, hydraulic fluids. I presented this to the House of Lords. The House of Lords commissioned an inquiry. I think they did commission research – they didn't give it to us, because they knew we were peddling this idea about organophosphates! Fair

> enough, I would have been biased! I wanted to find the cause. In total, I have seen sixteen pilots, ten more since, and that pattern is still the same. They are all very senior pilots – must have been exposed for more than six years. All of them reported incidents in the main cabin of a gas incident.
>
> The pattern of their autonomic signature is the same. I would have had some qualms if, out of the sixteen, two or three or four or five didn't have the similar pattern. But they all do. Now, of course a lot of statisticians would argue that it's a small sample, but so far it's 100 per cent. Then you really have to think very hard. If there were deaths, then definitely if there are one or two you will withdraw the product straight away, you wouldn't say: 'Oh, it's only one or two out of a population of 50 million.'

Although the pilots he studied had not died, they were suffering from serious, life-altering injuries. Dr Julu said:

> They mean a lot to the people concerned. The first captain whom I saw had a lot of wrangling with his airline. He was retired on health grounds, so he lost his income. He was accused of malingering. That was the main story. What we really have is the pattern of autonomic disturbance. These are based on examination; they are quantifiable and reproducible, and relate to autonomic functions. The patient cannot fake it. If it is somatic, you can say the patient is faking; unfortunately, these [autonomic disorders] are not fakeable. It is outside their control.

Dr Coxon's research

Dr Leonie Wilson Coxon, from Murdoch University in Perth, Western Australia, is a psychologist, and her research deals with tests on cognitive impairment. She published a PhD thesis in 2009 which gave details of her cognitive assessments on aircraft crew who reported symptoms following exposure to jet engine oil emissions.

The majority of participating aircrew showed impairments on tests of reaction time, processing speed and fine motor skills. A second study investigated the psychological impact on spouses of aircraft maintenance engineers affected by the toxic chemicals used in the de-seal/re-seal programme of a type of military aircraft. Some ninety-one spouses were assessed. The control was twenty-five age-matched spouses of other personnel at the same organization not involved in the programme. Results demonstrated significant differences between the experimental group and the control on matters such as anxiety, depression and stress. The experimental group 'had significant difficulties coping with spouses', Dr Coxon found.[10]

39

A lack of conclusive evidence?

One recent fume event was considered 'serious' by the UK Air Accidents Investigation Branch (AAIB) and was investigated by it. This occurred on 21 October 2012, on a Lufthansa Airbus A321 which had taken off from London Heathrow Airport. The two pilots noticed a strong smell and experienced dizziness, nausea and irritation to their eyes and throat. The fumes were bad enough that both the pilot and co-pilot were forced to use their oxygen masks. They called the purser into the cockpit, and she experienced similar symptoms, and also reported a smell. A few passengers complained of skin and throat irritation. The pilot and co-pilot managed to land the aircraft safely after it was given priority clearance. Six crew were sent to hospital for checks.

The AAIB report noted that the situation improved after the engines were shut down. The report, published in May 2013, added:

> This event thus joins a growing number of cases in which there has been a similar lack of conclusive evidence as to the cause(s) of aircraft cabin air quality issues.[1]

What further evidence could the AAIB and the CAA require in order to work out the cause?

Whose conspiracy theory?

Often, when a determined group of campaigners allege ongoing malpractice and cover-up by an entire industry, they are labelled conspiracy theorists. In the case of toxic cabin air, there is indeed a groundless conspiracy theory – but it operates the other way around from convention. It is created by the industry, and about the campaigners. Industry spokespeople have concocted a really fantastic story: that the countless number of people testifying to serious ill-health resulting directly from fume events, reporting similar symptoms to doctors in different continents, are all simultaneously 'hyperventilating', 'stressed', 'depressed' or otherwise suffering from some mental illness that causes them to display psychosomatic symptoms.

There is not a shred of evidence to support this absurd tale, the probability of the truth of which is vanishingly small. Those putting it forward, being in powerful positions, are never put under pressure to justify their line. It is extremely upsetting to those of us giving honest testimony that is dismissed in this insulting way.

Meanwhile, the threshold that the industry and governments set for aerotoxic campaigners to prove their case is nudged ever upwards towards infinity. Have we failed to prove our case?

As previously mentioned, there is a clearly identifiable syndrome – aerotoxic syndrome – which describes the symptoms experienced by countless individuals who travel as passengers or crew on aircraft. There can be no doubt that aircrew experience these symptoms together at a much higher level than the general population; indeed they experience them at a level only matched by other occupational groups with exposure to organophosphates, such as farmers handling insecticides and pesticides.

We know that exposure to organophosphates causes these symptoms, and we know that when those with the symptoms undergo physical tests, heightened levels of organophosphates are often found in their bodies.

We know too that there are organophosphate additives in aircraft engine oil. It is known that these substances are found at heightened levels in aircraft cabins even in normal operation, and even if airlines and aircraft manufacturers have managed to avoid the testing of the air during fume events, it is surely a reasonable assumption that when there are fumes in the cabin, they come from the engines. We know the mechanism by which this happens – leaks and failures in the bleed air system. And anyway, there are no realistic other possible sources of these fumes.

What do the deniers have to offer as an alternative? The

frankly ridiculous suggestion that a high proportion of intelligent, stable individuals in good jobs, and typically with no history whatsoever of mental problems, suddenly develop a consistent set of psychosomatic symptoms which just 'coincidentally' tend to follow on from their experience of fume events in aircraft.

If it was not that this attitude was destroying lives, we could describe it as ridiculous. Since it is destroying lives, it seems to me to be disgraceful and tragic.

40

An expert on chemical poisoning comments

Dr Michel Mulder (whom we met on page 100) once asked a mechanic at Schiphol to send him a dust filter from behind the ventilator of a fridge in the galley of a new KLM 777 after it had been replaced. He forwarded it to Professor Chris van Netten (a former member of the US National Research Council), who had begun a study into the effects of toxins in cabin air. This filter that had been exposed to aircraft air showed the same chemical profile as highly toxic jet engine oil ingredients, including tricresyl phosphate. Professor van Netten has frequently appeared as an expert witness on cases involving suspected chemical poisoning.

In an interview for this book, Professor van Netten said:

> You have an agent in the oil, that is a known neurotoxic agent .... It's unlikely that people are getting [this exposure] from another source. The likelihood is that it's from the engine oil, especially if it agrees with the maintenance records – you find that maintenance has changed the oil seals because they were leaking.
>
> So now we have: the agent, the route to exposure – i.e. leakage, if there is evidence of a smell or fumes in the cabin – and at the end you have the effect on the individuals, that are often consistent with the agent in the oils. It's difficult to see another explanation.
>
> The difficulty is, you're not talking about one agent, but a series. Another point is that, with the Birmingham and Malmo incidents [see pages 55–7 and 85–6], the pilots did not pass out because of tricresyl phosphate; it was mostly likely carbon monoxide. The others do not have an acute effect, there is often a delay with OPIDN [organophosphate-induced delay neuropathy]. It can take up to two weeks, so when the symptoms show, people may not make the connection.

When I'm an expert witness, they say, 'There was no evidence it was the exposure.' The reason is not because there was nothing in the air, just that we're not allowed to take measurements ... There are very few if any exposure measurements during these [fume] incidents.

41

Jet-lagged, travel fatigued or poisoned?

A couple of definitions:

> It has long been established that 'jet-lag' is primarily caused by crossing time zones in high speed jet aircraft, which results in temporary ill health symptoms such as sleep disruption, cognitive effects including poorer performance on mental tasks and concentration, increased fatigue, headaches, irritability, and problems with digestion.
>
> Meanwhile, travel fatigue is general fatigue, disorientation and headache caused by a disruption in routine, time spent in a cramped space with little chance to move around, a low-oxygen environment, and dehydration caused by limited food and dry air. It does not necessarily have the shift in circadian rhythms that cause jet lag. Travel fatigue can occur without crossing time zones, and it often disappears after a single day accompanied by a night of high-quality sleep.[1]

It is convenient for airlines that when people who have flown experience these kinds of symptom, they typically put it down to jet-lag (or if they have not actually crossed time zones, but flown north–south or south–north, to more general travel fatigue). But should long-distance travel actually have this kind of impact on people's health? No one has really challenged this idea since the jet age began in the 1950s.

The definitions above include a catch-all of the problems people regularly experience after flights, especially long-distance flights. Sometimes these symptoms disappear quickly, as the quote suggests, but sometimes they persist for days, weeks and years afterwards.

Perhaps we should look more carefully at what symptoms can be attributed to a change of routine or of time zone, and what symptoms are more likely to have a different cause. Tiredness after a long flight, and a delay before you feel fully adapted to the new daily rhythm? That sounds like jet-lag to me. But cognitive problems, difficulties concentrating, headaches, irritability: is it really the case that these are caused by being in a cramped low-oxygen environment and breathing dry air for a few hours, then adapting to a different time zone? And when some people experience significant problems for a long time after a flight, and others (or even the same people, after different flights) have no difficulties at all, is it right to put these symptoms down to the general in-flight environment? I think it is much more likely that in reality, those who believe they are suffering from particularly bad jet-lag have been unknowingly poisoned by toxic oil fumes in the air they breathed on the airplane.

It is widely accepted now that smoking tobacco, and even secondary smoking (being exposed to fumes from other people smoking), can have a bad effect on our health. As a result lighting-up is banned in workplaces, cafes, bars and restaurants in many countries, and there is an increasing move to ban it in outdoor public places. It should be equally apparent that prolonged or repeated exposure to highly toxic oil fumes in the confined space of a jet may cause the types of symptom we have called aerotoxic syndrome. Writing them down to 'jet-lag' does us no favours at all.

After all, way back in 1955 before I was born, US scientists had concluded that exposure to oil fume events could have this kind of effect. And Professor Solly Zuckerman from the UK recommended that all organophosphate containers should be marked 'Deadly Poison'. Instead we seem to be going on the opposite direction: as we saw on page 29, the health and safety warnings on jet engine oil cans have recently been cynically removed.

42

What the airlines know

Former stewardess Dee Passon, whose story I told in Chapter 11, went on to say:

> With BA it makes me so angry that they have all this evidence, and yet they say they can't find the causal link – but it's only because they don't look; they're not looking for the causal link. You have filters – they're called crew. You could do a blood test before a flight and a blood test after a flight, and see the difference.[1]

Dee recalls a major study carried out by RAF personnel in the 1980s, into the health of BA crew. She says:

> It got completely squashed. Not even those who took part were told the results. Years later, in 2007, I was working with one of the people who took part. I asked, 'What happened to it?' They took lots of tests, but they wouldn't tell anyone the results. It was carried out by RAF medical specialists I think. People had been told at the beginning that they were going to know the results. I joined in 1984. We knew all about it [the survey]. Doctors were meeting people after flights, taking blood pressure and so on. Doctors were going on some flights themselves. I don't know what prompted it [the survey]. But we never heard another thing about it.

Perhaps it is time to unearth the results. Dee is convinced, however, that the link between toxins in cabin air and high sickness levels among cabin crew became more widely appreciated by BA managers around 2006:

> It ties in with when Tristan [Loraine] got sick. Up until then they were banging on about the high rate of sickness of cabin crew, saying things like 'We are 7 per cent above the national average.' Shouting from the roof-tops. Then suddenly, they

> went quiet. Stopped complaining. There was a new absence management policy introduced, that could stop you from having too much sickness; they made it much harder to get an ill health pension.

A newsletter sent out to cabin services directors by a British Airways manager in 2005 included a section on staff absence, which reads:

> The cabin crew absence levels have remained consistently higher than the company and national average. This is a huge concern to our business due to the operational and manpower disruption it causes. In addition we face a considerable employee cost reduction target and a reduction in absence is key contributor to this.[2]

It is noticeable that the management concern expressed here is entirely about costs. It's not about the poor staff who are being made sick by their jobs. Indeed, it carries the menacing implication that illness is somehow the crew member's fault. Such total disregard for employee welfare is not only unethical, but contrary to the employer's duty of care under UK health and safety legislation.

Dee had had an exemplary record of almost twenty years' service with British Airways. In common with all the other sufferers of aerotoxic syndrome whom I have known over the years, she struggled in to work over a long period despite her painful symptoms. In 2009 she wrote to the chief executive of British Airways, Willie Walsh, quizzing him about what she perceived to be the high sickness and death rates of cabin crew. She was sacked shortly afterwards. 'I never received a reply,' Dee told me, 'but I'm told my email caused quite a stir.'

The 'tombstone' email

I have in my possession an internal Boeing email from 2007. It was sent by George Bates, of Boeing Environmental Controls, to several colleagues on 26 October 2007. It reveals that fume events were occurring on B757s with particular engine configurations every two weeks, and that even internally to Boeing, information was lacking about their chemical composition. He expresses surprise that the (US) Federal Aviation Administration has never acted. (There is some technical jargon in the email, but the gist should be clear.) It reads as follows:

> I have not been signing for Toxicity other than to make sure my parts have MI numbers. Hydraulic Mist is another toxic product I refuse to get involved with even though our recirc filters have the capability to coalesce the mist. Further, the situation has not changed from what Brian has described.
>
> I will add the Propulsion folks do not account or certify the bleed air quality they feed to us. For the 747-8, John Klym was the most recent to try to get the Propulsion folks to step up to owning their system by-products. All he got was the run around like I got in 2000 for the 767-400. Pratt & Whitney has some guarantees in their spec but GE and Rolls-Royce engine specs do not mention bleed air quality when it comes to CO/CO_2 or hydrocarbon by-products. The Engine Specs are the hole no one has addressed.
>
> Given the number of COSP events for the 757/RB211-535C & -535E engines resulting from failed Fan and Forward IFC Bearing Oil Seals allowing oil by-products in the bleed ducts, I would have thought the FAA [Federal Aviation Administration] would have forced the issue.
>
> With all diversions (about 1 every 2 weeks) and Return to Base events due to Haze in the Cabin, I would have thought the FAA would have made the Engine Manufacturers address this by now. Some of the 757 events have been pretty significant in that the crew reported blue smoke with defined waves in the smoke. The visibility was limited so that the attendants in the aft galley could not see to the mid cabin over-wing exits. This is more than a light haze that we debate endlessly about for smoke evacuation. Who knows what the by-products are in hot synthetic Turbine Oil. The Material Data Sheet has warnings about skin contact and breathing the fumes of the oil, let alone the complication of partial combustion products.
>
> The 767 / GE CF6-80A and 747 / GE CF6-80E airplane and engine combinations are better than Rolls-Royce as far as frequency, but it still happens. The thing to note is the wide body events are nowhere as severe or dense as the 757 has experienced. The common theme is these are mostly old

> engines more than 15 years old. While SACO has informally discussed with me the widebody events, the thing I took away from the FAA/SACO [Seattle Aircraft Certification Office] discussion is the New England FAA is not interested in following up or supporting SACO on these events that are generally resulting from out of production engines. Bottom line is I think we are looking for a tombstone before anyone with any horsepower is going to take interest.

The ARDOF Committee at KLM

An internal KLM health services document, leaked to the Dutch Zembla web TV channel, states that contaminated fumes may get into the cabin. Zembla discovered that a special working party has been set up by KLM called ARDOF, an acronym for the English name 'Aircraft Related Dangerous Oil Fumes'.

Ton Scherrenberg, chair of the KLM staff union, said in a documentary, aired on Zembla in May 2013, 'It is being discussed internally, but always behind closed doors. Within the working party, which is autonomous and never discloses anything.' Peter Hartman, the then CEO of KLM (he stood down in July 2013), regularly attended these meetings, Mr Scherrenberg told the Zembla documentary. The programme also revealed that in the Netherlands, there were ninety-seven fume events officially recorded in 2007, with forty reported cases of consequent illness.[3]

Airbus conducts monitoring

One source told me:

> Airbus has been flying around at least one aircraft – some reports say more than one – for some time now, with a full gas chromatography mass-spectrometry machine aboard, doing real time constant measuring of air quality. These are £2m-plus machines and it has probably been going on for at least a year. To my knowledge they have never yet revealed even their interim findings .... One would think that if they

were in a position to report a perfectly safe environment they would be shouting it from the roof-tops.

One airline executive breaks ranks

In the Netherlands, there is more discussion and awareness of fume events and consequent ill-health than in many other countries. The Felderhof-KLM case was summarized in Chapter 37. Another intriguing development has come at the budget carrier ArkeFly. The chief executive, Steven van der Heijden, broke ranks with other airline executives in acknowledging the risks openly. In May 2013 he said, 'It is well known that high concentrations of oil fumes can put pilots in a state in which they can hardly land the aircraft. That affects flight safety. It is of the greatest importance that we overcome this.' He gave his backing to medical research among the aircrew: 'You do not want people to get sick or less able to fly a plane.'[4]

43

Pressure on politicians

We all know that industries employ lobbyists and other staff whose objective is to influence politicians to make decisions and statements that suit their interests. It is more rare, though, to see the process in action. Here is a story that shows how the process can work.

The chair of the 1999–2000 Australian Senate inquiry into cabin air, retired Senator Reverend John Woodley, gave an interview for this book. He describes the relentless pressure from the industry to suppress debate, and attempts to denigrate the character of expert witnesses testifying as to the hazards in cabin air and the impact on human health. Revd Woodley said:

> There are millions if not billions at stake in fixing the problem and that doesn't even begin to deal with health issues of, perhaps, thousands of people. The airlines, governments, insurance companies and manufacturers have colluded, I believe, to make sure that they never admit that they know the cause of the problem.[1]

Revd Woodley was particularly interested in showing how civil servants are pressured to draft reports in the way the industry would prefer. Indeed, in some cases the civil servants these days are themselves seconded from the industry itself. In his words:

> There's always a public servant to resource these kinds of committees. When he wrote the [draft] report, I couldn't believe it – it had none of these issues; none of the evidence. I can only say that he was got at. I took the report and wrote it in my office. I got my staff to read all the evidence and get advice, and we wrote it ourselves. It [the earlier version] was just a whitewash, so we wrote the report ourselves. We put it to the committee of elected parliamentarians and it was unanimous. They went through it clause by clause. That was the evidence that we had received.

Rev. Woodley was also concerned about one particular witness who was allowed to give evidence, even though – contrary to the usual protocol – he had not made a written submission against which Senate panel members could frame their questions. He recalls:

> We couldn't work out how he got there, because he hadn't made a written submission – normally we would question them on their written submission. He spent half an hour denigrating all the people who had appeared to give evidence to us. Finally we said that we didn't want to hear from him any more. Then we discovered that he was being paid by the insurance companies to defend court cases regarding compensation for flight attendants or pilots. I understand that he had got to appear before our inquiry because he approached the public servant.

After the Senate's highly critical report was published, of course, the next challenge was to see action follow it. The Australian government kicked the issue into the very long grass, and few if any of the proposals were acted upon.

Revd Woodley picked up a similar pattern at the UK House of Lords inquiry in 2007, when he visited London and met with the chairperson, Baroness Wilcox:

> Baroness Wilcox asked to see me. Before I saw her I met a public servant, who was charming, but from the way he was talking to me, he was downplaying the problems. My wife and I had lunch with Baroness Wilcox, and she asked, 'What do you think?' I replied, 'You're being snowed. Be very careful of the public servants assisting you.' Sure enough, her report was just another whitewash.

44

A good look at a dissenter

One of the most high-profile critics of the theory that aerotoxic syndrome is a widespread problem caused by fume leaks is Michael Bagshaw, visiting professor of aviation medicine at Kings College London, former chief medical officer for British Airways, and advisor to airlines and related bodies including BA, the UK CAA, Cranfield, BALPA, Airbus and the (UK) Building Research Establishment (BRE).[1] Coincidentally, he was the doctor who grounded me in 2006 (see Chapter 15). He posted (on the web) a long article (never peer-reviewed, successively updated through 2013) which sets out the case for and against aerotoxic syndrome, and concludes that there is insufficient evidence for such a diagnosis. He declined an invitation to be interviewed for this book, but sent me what was at the time of writing the latest version of this paper, version 2.6, dated October 2013.[2] In fairness to the dissenting viewpoint I summarize here the main points it makes.

The paper acknowledges the reports made by pilots and flight attendants of ill-health following fume leaks, describing the symptoms as 'mainly acutely irritant in nature', without citing a source for that particular point. Bagshaw adds, 'less frequently, some aircrew report longer-term symptoms. However, the epidemiological evidence is hampered by inconsistency in reporting and the numbers are small.' In 2013, he noted, twenty-eight UK professional pilots are on a CAA database 'who have suggested an association between illness and the cabin environment', according to the CAA Safety Regulation Group (SRG) Medical Department. On 4 October 2010 I received a letter from Chief Medical Officer Dr Sally Evans confirming that I was present on this database. Four years later, I am in the process of finding out the present number of pilots on the database, although I note with regret that similar databases do not exist for cabin crew or passengers.

The paper discusses just one group of potential toxins in

jet engine oil, the tricresyl phosphate group of compounds, but does so in some depth, describing the toxicity of different isomers. It then cites a succession of studies indicating that the levels of TCP on aircraft are very low, lower than is found in some other environments. It mentions several times that fume events are estimated to occur on one in 2,000 flights on average.

Bagshaw does mention the research by Schindler and colleagues (see pages 163–4) and Professor Abou-Donia (see pages 161–2) that I have summarized in this book, but he argues that their findings are inconclusive. There is no reference to the two studies by Dr Sarah Mackenzie Ross, or to the 100-plus diagnoses of aerotoxic syndrome made by independent clinics around the world. There is a long section on human toxicology, and the possible impact of pressurized cabin air on the effect of toxins on the human body.

One section introduces the possibility that hyperventilation is an explanation for some of the symptoms reported. The paper states, 'Obviously, not every case of "aerotoxic syndrome" [the inverted commas are his] is caused by hyperventilation, but it offers a plausible explanation for some reported events.'[3]

One possible reason for hyperventilation coming into consideration is that breathing difficulties can occur in those affected by toxins of this nature. But research carried out by Dr Peter Julu has shown that this is a symptom of toxic injury, not a psychosomatic feature.[4] The hyperventilation hypothesis is similarly rebutted by respiratory expert Dr Jonathan Burdon in a letter to BALPA.[5]

At least Professor Bagshaw makes a public contribution to the debate. His paper makes some interesting points, but the main problem that the Aerotoxic Association's scientific advisers have with it is one of omission. He does not acknowledge the high levels of toxins that have been found in people diagnosed with aerotoxic syndrome. And it seems to us that it is circular reasoning to argue that the number of pilots who are listed as suffering from aerotoxic syndrome is low. As we have seen, the industry (including its medical staff) generally refuses to acknowledge that aerotoxic syndrome exists, so it is hardly surprising that they rarely diagnose it. It would be more useful to find out how many pilots and other aircrew reporting sick suffered from symptoms that fit this diagnosis.

To quote an average occurrence of fume events does not seem to me helpful. First, as we have seen, fume events fall on such a wide spectrum that it is almost impossible to determine accurately how many occur. And second, some aircraft/engine combinations are much worse than others, so this is an average of a wide range. Even so, one event in every 2,000 flights is not a low figure. If once in every 2,000 journeys a make of automobile filled with fumes, sometimes so bad that they incapacitated its driver, there would surely be an immediate product recall. By what succession of tiny steps have we convinced ourselves in the aviation industry that such appalling lapses of product quality are acceptable?

Note too that apart from raising the possibility of psychosomatic causes, Professor Bagshaw does not have a credible alternative explanation of the range of symptoms that aircrew and passengers report. Many of these are not typical symptoms of stress, depression or chronic fatigue syndrome.

Nonetheless, Professor Bagshaw posted his paper and shared it with me. He also appeared on the Australian television programme *60 Minutes*, which screened on 1 December 2013, and endured some difficult questions.

In addition, he exchanged a long series of emails with me during the peer review process for this book (although, as you will see, he declined to be a formal peer reviewer). I am reproducing them in full (apart from the openings and closings, which were consistently friendly, but do not contribute to the meat of the argument) to ensure that Professor Bagshaw's views are given in their entirety. (References in the body of his emails have been moved to the notes in this book.) Although I was unable to agree with his opinions, I am most grateful for his patience in responding to my questions repeatedly and at considerable length.

John Hoyte to Professor Bagshaw, 14 August 2014

I am writing to give you an advance proof copy of my forthcoming book *Aerotoxic Syndrome: Aviation's Darkest Secret.*

The book is a semi-autobiographical work on the Aerotoxic issue and includes my discovery of the illness, testimonies of other aircrew and passengers affected, along with the science and politics.

The book is a 3 hour read and written to enlighten a layman, who has never heard of Aerotoxic Syndrome.

Professional ghost writers and editors have been working on this book for just over a year now and prior to full publication I hope that you would agree to be one of my professional peer-reviewers ...

Professor Bagshaw to John Hoyte, 2 September 2014

Thank you for your email and the advance proof copy of your forthcoming book. I am flattered that you have asked me to provide a peer review.

After careful consideration, in fairness to you I must decline your request for the following reasons.

You will remember that we first met in February 2006 when I was asked to prepare a report for your management at flybe International following your long period of sickness absence. You had been examined by the flybe occupational medical adviser who gave an opinion that you were suffering from a personality disorder bordering on psychiatric illness and were unfit to fly.

Subsequently you were examined by the CAA Consultant Psychiatrist whose opinion was that you showed no psychiatric pathology, but a normal reaction to stress.

Following your consultation with me, we agreed that you had suffered an acute-on-chronic affective stress disorder which made you unfit to exercise the privileges of a Class 1 medical certificate, exacerbated by unfortunate events involving publication of a safety report. Away from the commercial flying environment, we noted that you were fit and well. However, I felt that re-exposure to the commercial flying environment would lead to a recurrence of your stress symptoms and signs and you were likely to again become unfit.

You agreed with this diagnosis and these conclusions and you retired on the grounds of ill health.

Checking my notes of our consultation, there was no discussion of fume exposure or any mention of the so-called 'aerotoxic syndrome'.

You will be aware that, together with the majority of aviation medical practitioners and clinical toxicologists worldwide, I cannot accept that the wide range of symptoms and signs reported by a small number of crew members are the result of neurotoxicity caused by organophosphate inhalation.

The toxic effects of organophosphates are specific and are due to impairment of neurotransmission in the peripheral nerves, giving rise to muscular weakness and paralysis. In terms of medical toxicology, it is impossible to explain the wide range of symptoms and signs reported by some crew members as a unified result of TCP exposure.

Symptoms reported by some crew members who have been exposed to fumes in the cabin, particularly when emergency oxygen masks are used, are the same as those seen in acute or chronic hyperventilation. Obviously not every case of 'aerotoxic syndrome' is caused by hyperventilation, but it offers a plausible explanation for some reported events.

In some cases, the symptoms may be due to irritation associated with enhanced chemical sensitivity to certain volatile organic compounds.

The reported symptoms are wide-ranging with insufficient consistency to justify the establishment of a medical syndrome. It has been noted that many of the acute symptoms are normal symptoms experienced by most people frequently; some 70% of the population experience one or more of them on any given day.

Individuals can vary in their response to potential toxic insult because of age, health status, previous exposure or genetic differences.

In addition, it can be difficult to disentangle the physical, psychological and emotional components of well-being, and there is no doubt that different people will respond in different ways on different occasions.

It is not understood why most occupants of pressurised aircraft do not report symptoms despite having the same exposure as those who do; there are few, if any, reports from passengers.

Finally, so far as scientific evidence has been able to establish to date, the amounts of organophosphates to which aircraft crew members could be exposed, even over multiple, long-term exposures, are insufficient to produce neurotoxicity.

Investigations of aircraft cabin air world-wide have failed to detect levels of TCP above well-established and validated occupational exposure limit values. The partial pressure in the lung alveolar gas mixture of any TCP contamination of the cabin air is so low that it is unlikely to cross the alveolar membrane.

Genetic or particular susceptibility to a particular adverse effect of certain chemicals on the part of an individual does not alter the need for there to have been a sufficient chemical exposure to cause the injury or damage. It has been shown that the possible exposure levels to ToCP on aircraft are so low relative to what is required to create a toxic effect through inhalation that a toxic injury is simply not medically feasible with current understanding.

Any form of illness can be disabling whether it occurs through toxicity or through nocebo effects, and therefore we agree that there is a continuing imperative to minimise the risk of fume incidents that give rise to symptoms.

Aviation medical professionals throughout the world continue to monitor the scientific evidence and remain receptive to objective peer-reviewed evidence. I retain an open mind.

John Hoyte to Professor Bagshaw, 8 September 2014

Thank you for your reply and confirming important detail from 2005 which I had overlooked, but will be most helpful in the book.

I wonder if you would mind answering the following questions for my understanding of medical procedures; for inclusion in the book and as formal evidence in the future:

Yes/No answers will suffice for Questions 1 and 2.

1. In late 2005, BALPA offered me the choice of either you, as an experienced aviation doctor or Captain Julian Soddy of BALPA and a former KLM UK BAe 146 pilot as potential assessors for my 'Loss of licence' payment.

I decided to choose you, as I was keen to have expert medical opinion and advice to help me understand the cause of the sudden onset of ill health from 1990 onwards to 2006 and beyond.

I recall being confused that Capt. Soddy had been put forward by BALPA as a LOL assessor as it seemed to be a medical assessment. I did not know Capt. Soddy at the time and had no idea of the significance of his background, which I later discovered and can be read in a 20th January 2004 'OP Report' (attached), Capt. Soddy features on page 15. He also chaired the BALPA Contaminated Air London conference of

April 2005 and has made several media appearances regarding contaminated air such as BBC *Panorama*'s programme 'Something in the air' in 2008. https://www.youtube.com/watch?v=3dsDznr4z5w

I have since learnt that international scientific literature was published before I was born in the mid 1950s which describes how exposure to oil fumes in a confined space can cause serious ill health in some people.

My question is whether you had personal understanding of this possible cause of ill health in early February 2006, when you reported on my ill health for Loss of Licence purpose? Y/N?

2. Would you be willing to be repeatedly exposed to visible jet engine oil fumes in a confined space on the ground in order to demonstrate your support of the present mainstream medical opinion that adverse health effects are 'uncertain'? Y/N ?

3. How are professional aircrew, who have a duty to report possible causes of ill health for the benefit of others, expected to communicate their ill health symptoms to medical doctors?

I look forward to receiving your answers before the 12th September 2014 for incorporation in the book.

Professor Bagshaw to John Hoyte, 9 September 2014

As a Fellow of the Faculty of Occupational Medicine and a registered specialist in occupational medicine I am of course familiar with the toxicology of organophosphates and the risks to health when ingested or absorbed in large quantities. The levels so far detected in aircraft cabin air are of such low levels that it is simply physiologically impossible for them to be absorbed by inhalation. When we met in 2005, none of the symptoms you described were related to the peripheral neurotoxicity which would result from organophosphate poisoning.

So the answer to your first question is yes, I was aware of this possible cause of ill health but my clinical judgement was that it was not the cause of your symptoms.

With regard to your second question, as an 8000 hour ATPL holder I have had my share of fume events without any apparent health effects.

For your final question, aircrew have a duty to report any ill health affecting their fitness to fly and this is usually done via their AME or direct to the CAA Medical Department. Any health concerns should be discussed with the AME – you do not have to wait for the next scheduled medical examination.

John Hoyte to Professor Bagshaw, 10 September 2014

In question 3, I was not trying to understand the actual lines of communication, which I'm well familiar with but rather how aircrew are meant to describe their actual ill health symptoms to medical doctors?

In early 2006 for example, my speech and word finding were poor, a very bad memory, a continual echo in my head, thought processing difficulties, sweating, extreme fatigue and blurred vision among other symptoms. Most of these symptoms were filmed for 45 minutes in 2001 on a Training Captain's course and my course mates rightly criticised my embarrassing performance.

These were difficult symptoms to express by definition and it's even harder now to communicate the fact that they have now mostly disappeared over the past 8 years – except for the sweating which has been with me since early 1990.

When I began to understand the probable cause of my serious ill health in early 2006 and afterwards I made signed statements and 'sworn testimonies' at solicitors for the various responsible Authorities all of which have been ignored or trivialised.

This leaves a professional pilot wondering how one is supposed to pass on such safety critical information, which may help a doctor understand a particular disease not only for that aircrew but for the benefit of others.

This is particularly important to me as I have recently returned to Flying Instructing, where absolute integrity dictates that I have to counsel other aspiring pilots on how deal with the effects of oil smoke fumes and the actual causes of hyper-ventilation etc.

At the moment I am concerned that 'my word is not my bond' – according to some doctors, which for me is a serious issue for which I require some practical guidance, please.

Once again, how are professional pilots expected to communicate their ill health symptoms to medical doctors?

Professor Bagshaw to John Hoyte, 11 September 2014

Apologies for the delayed response; you raise an important question.

Anybody with unexplained symptoms or signs causing concern should present and explain them to their medical practitioner. It is important to maintain an open mind of causation and to trust the professionalism of the practitioner to reach an appropriate diagnosis. The consultation should begin with a clean sheet of paper with no preconceived ideas by either patient or doctor. As the diagnostic process evolves, the doctor may well refer the patient on for specialist investigation; again it is important to maintain an open mind on both sides.

The process of medical diagnosis and treatment follows a well-established practice in which the patient presents the symptoms and signs, together with the history, to the medical practitioner. The subsequent diagnostic process involves the determination of the nature of the disease based on known patterns and the outcome of well-validated clinical tests, taking into account knowledge and experience of human pathology and treatment. It is normal for the medical practitioner and patient to work together, going through a process of differential diagnosis to eventually arrive at a result.

The difficulties which have arisen with the medical profession and the supposed 'aerotoxic syndrome' include the inconsistency and wide range of symptoms and signs reported by many of those who believe they are affected. Organophosphate poisoning gives rise to specific and well understood peripheral neurotoxicity, and many of the reported symptoms simply do not result from this type of poisoning – a medical fact. Thus for an individual affected to present to the medical practitioner declaring they are suffering effects of such poisoning impedes the normal diagnostic process, introducing distrust on both sides.

Another fact is that the maximum concentrations in the lung alveoli of organophosphates originating in engine bleed air exert insufficient partial pressure to pass through the alveolar membrane for absorption. Organophosphate poisoning occurs via ingestion, not inhalation. This is based on the established laws of physiology and physics.

The medical profession recognises the fact that a number of crew members have suffered health problems, both acute and chronic. While many well-documented cases can be explained by the normal human response of hyperventilation, there are some cases which cannot. It is unfortunate that the hostility directed towards some of the aviation medical profession has led in many cases to a breakdown in trust, rather than a working together to seek diagnosis and treatment of the affected individuals. The open mind must be maintained on both sides, with a recognition of specialist clinical knowledge and experience; other causes must be sought for ill health.

Unfortunately, much of the scientific data presented in support of the hypothesis that contaminated cabin air causes the supposed 'aerotoxic syndrome' do not stand up to scientific scrutiny. Independent academic review shows research design biased in favour of predetermined agenda, failure to compare results from an 'exposed' group to a 'non-exposed' group, and unscientific sampling with unsupportable conclusions – a causative link between reported health symptoms and engine oil toxicity is not demonstrated by the research.

Finally, the reported claims of bias and cover up by the medical professional are particularly offensive – ultimately doctors are accountable to their patients and to their independent regulatory body who grant their registration, and they have to work within the ethical boundaries of their specialist college. Ideally we should all work together to determine the cause of ill health and seek to find a solution, without the bias of preconceived ideas.

John Hoyte to Professor Bagshaw, 12 September 2014

Many thanks for your explanation.

As we are both instructing pilots, could you possibly help me with one of my previous points:

This is particularly important to me as I have recently returned to Flying Instructing, where absolute integrity dictates that I have to counsel other aspiring pilots on how deal with the effects of oil smoke fumes and the actual causes of hyperventilation etc.

I am extremely conscious of the necessity for joined-up safety information for aspiring pilots and my idea of certain 'threats' and their management are not what I have found in the text books.

How should I be teaching my pilots to deal with my perceived threat of oil smoke fumes in a confined space and the causes of hyperventilation?

Professor Bagshaw to John Hoyte, 15 September 2014

Again my apologies for the slow response – displaying Bulldog formation aerobatics at White Waltham at the weekend so been busy practising.

I agree with the importance of joined-up safety information for all pilots and I have always respected your absolute integrity. It is unfortunate that so much misunderstanding has raised the emotional level in the community, so it is good to discuss things with you as a fellow instructor on a factual level.

I'll give you some of my thoughts, and forgive me stating many of the things you already know.

The potential silent killer in fumes from the internal combustion engine is of course carbon monoxide, which is odourless and colourless, and produced by incomplete combustion of carbonaceous material. It is present in the exhaust fumes of piston engines and so may be associated with gases and fumes which can be detected by smell or sight. It is highly poisonous because of the ease with which it combines with haemoglobin in the red blood cells.

Each aircraft type will have a fumes drill, which for light G/A aircraft generally involves:

- Shut off the cabin air heater
- Open all sources of fresh air to the cabin (DV panels, windows)
- If oxygen is available (unlikely in a PA28 or C152!), should be used by all occupants
- Land asap
- Seek medical advice if headache, nausea, dizziness and/or reduction in vision (note that these symptoms can also result from hyperventilation – see later).

Products of combustion in a turbine engine do not usually include carbon monoxide, and I am aware that it is the combustion product of the jet engine oil additives which is the cause of concern, particularly organophosphates. As I and other aviation medicine specialists and clinical toxicologists have shown, there is simply insufficient organophosphate present in cabin air (even during a fume event) to be absorbed via the lungs and cause neurotoxicity. But obviously prolonged exposure to smoke and fumes is not a good idea.

The sense of smell is an important protective mechanism and, in the human, the smell will be detected at concentration levels 1000 times less than the toxic or harmful level of a volatile substance. So generally the fact that you can smell something doesn't necessarily mean it is doing you any harm, but acts as a warning trigger.

There are individual genetic sensitivities to chemicals and smells. For example I am sensitive to coffee and the smell of coffee fumes gives me a headache and a muzzy head – that does not mean that coffee is harmful and should be universally banned (although personally I would welcome that!). It is perfectly feasible that the smell of oil fumes could have a similar effect on some individuals, but that doesn't mean that it necessarily causes harm to their health.

Again, each aircraft type will have a specific QRH drill in the event of smoke or fumes. The common factor of course is to don the emergency oxygen mask so that by breathing 100% oxygen inhalation of cabin air is avoided. As we both know, the mask usually incorporates some form of eye protection.

So now we have the situation where there is anxiety about the source of the smoke or fumes, the unfamiliarity of using an oxygen mask with its resistance to breathing, difficulty using the R/T because of mask and ambient noise, difficulty reading the instruments and charts because of the smoke goggles and a general increase in arousal as the emergency drill is performed. The perfectly normal human response is to release adrenaline, one of the effects of which is to hyperventilate in preparation for running away from the threatening sabre toothed tiger.

Hyperventilation simply means breathing in excess of the metabolic needs of the body, which removes carbon dioxide from the bloodstream faster than it is being produced by metabolism. This leads to a change in blood acidity and associated chemical changes throughout the body, particularly in the nervous system. The fight or flight response prepares the body for an imminent increase in physical activity and the hyperventilation is part of this response.

As any textbook of aviation medicine or human performance will tell you, causes of hyperventilation include:

- Anxiety
- Stress
- Excitement
- Pressure breathing and unfamiliarity using a mask
- Motion sickness
- Vibration
- Heat
- Acceleration (G forces)
- Hypoxia.

The symptoms associated with hyperventilation include:

- Dizziness
- Increased sensation of body heat
- Tingling sensation in the fingers and toes
- Increased heart rate
- Nausea
- Blurred vision
- Deterioration in mental and physical performance.

In extreme cases, muscular spasm can occur in the fingers and toes and this can lead to loss of consciousness. When this happens the breathing rate slows and respiration becomes normal again with rapid recovery. There is then nothing to find on medical examination because the body has reverted to its normal state.

The symptoms can be very alarming and the individual understandably may truly believe that damage has occurred to the nervous system, particularly when medical examination fails to find any cause. This in itself leads to anxiety, which causes a low level of hyperventilation and some of the symptoms to persist. Which leads to more anxiety .... etc. etc.

It has been shown that 20–40% of student aircrew suffer from hyperventilation at some stage during flying training and, as explained, it is common in experienced aircrew during an in-flight emergency or when being trained to operate a new aircraft type or during sim and line checks. It is important that pilots understand what it is and that it is a perfectly normal human response. Pilots need to be aware of how it is caused, and learn to relax and reduce the breathing rate when symptoms or signs are recognised. I am sure this is part of your normal instructional technique.

So to attempt to answer your question, in the event of smoke or fumes, follow the drills to avoid breathing the contaminated air either by opening the DV panel or breathing 100% oxygen. Expect symptoms and signs of hyperventilation – this a normal human response. Consciously try to relax and reduce the breathing rate. If symptoms and signs persist after the event, consult an AME or general medical practitioner as discussed previously. Remember that hyperventilation is a normal human reaction to any adverse or unfamiliar situation.

John Hoyte to Professor Bagshaw, 15 September 2014

Thank you once again for your medical explanations, which I found most intriguing.

As the Peer Review process for my book on Aerotoxic Syndrome is approaching the end, would it be possible to publish your advice for a wider audience, as it contains significant insights into aspects of aviation medicine which are at variance to certain published scientific evidence?

A simple Yes/No will suffice. Thank you again for your assistance.

Professor Bagshaw to John Hoyte, 16 September 2014

I am glad you found my explanations to be of interest.

In fact everything I have explained is normal physiology and physics and is written in all the main-stream textbooks. It is actually some of the recently published evidence which is at variance with the well-established medical understanding; I regret to say that some of it does not stand up to independent unbiased academic scrutiny.

Following my outrageous mauling at the hands of an Australian TV journalist, I am now cautious about being publically quoted and being taken out of context. My advice is already published in my book 'Human Performance and Limitations in Aviation' and in other similar texts. On the understanding that it is not distorted or taken out of context I am of course happy for my advice to be further quoted.

John Hoyte to Professor Bagshaw, 17 September 2014

Thank you for allowing me to quote you and I will use all of your advice, do not worry.

Having read your previous comments carefully I would like to ask you three key questions in a set order, which are fundamental, yet remain unanswered to date – despite Freedom of Information (FOI) requests.

1. You state that: 'As I and other aviation medicine specialists and clinical toxicologists have shown, there is simply insufficient organophosphate present in cabin air (even during a fume event) to be absorbed via the lungs and cause neurotoxicity.'

My question is that for 16 years I personally witnessed countless visible oil fume events (photographs and videos exist of visible oil fume events) both on the ground and in the air and I offered to fill a BAe 146 with visible oil fumes on the ground in November 2007 for testing. Whilst you and others have shown that the concentrations of organophosphates in either so-called 'normal' air or non fume event flights are 'very low'.

Would you please forward to me for publication the actual concentrations of organophosphates and other chemicals (micrograms per cubic meter) in a visible oil fume event, along with your associated scale of Low to High?

2. Medical opinion has changed over the past 50 years to accept now that primary, secondary and tertiary exposure to tobacco smoke is a health hazard, whilst exposure to visible oil smoke or fumes in a confined space is somehow not a health hazard.

Do you accept that if the actual data to Question 1 were used, it could also explain similar illness caused by an oil fume event in a jet aircraft?

3. http://aerotoxic.org/wp-content/uploads/2014/01/MS17.pdf MS17 was published by the UK Government in 2000 (First edition 1980) and lists the symptoms of 'Medical aspects of work-related exposures to organophosphates'. I experienced sudden onset of many of the symptoms whilst flying the BAe 146 from 1990–2005, but now most of the symptoms (apart from my temperature control) have resolved. I feel I have a duty to pass on my experience to the Government, for the benefit of others.

'It is not understood why most occupants of pressurised aircraft do not report symptoms despite having the same exposure as those who do; there are few, if any, reports from passengers.'

It is respectfully suggested that occupants (including

children) do not report symptoms but suffer in silence due to an ongoing lack of understanding by doctors, an unwillingness to use appropriate tests and logic that genetic variability will be affected differently, as with all other chemical insults whether by 'drug' or by coffee. Whilst some doctors frequently state that they do not know the cause of certain illnesses, to ignore a likely cause appears irresponsible.

Professional pilots have a strong sense of duty of care, integrity and the precautionary principle – it is only when these values are challenged that we feel obliged to question some doctors' opinions.

Most citizens expect genuine research, healthy debate in public, where all of the actual evidence is examined by neutrals before a conclusion is agreed.

Do you understand why the present position would be offensive to professional pilots, who are attempting to protect the health of children, and who have a duty to pass on publicly available evidence to doctors?

I particularly look forward to receiving your answer to Question 1, which for me is basic data.

Professor Bagshaw to John Hoyte, 17 September 2014

1. The concerns have all been raised with respect to the ortho isomer of TCP and the supposed neuro-toxic effects, which is where I have concentrated my data gathering. I have also witnessed and experienced many visible oil fume events in my 40-plus year career in aviation.

The reported concentration of TCP used in most aircraft engine oils is less than 3%, of which the ortho isomers constitute less than 0.2% of the total TCP. This results in an overall concentration of ortho isomers of less than 0.006% of the total engine oil.[6]

Consequently TCP mixtures used in engine oils are significantly less toxic than pure ToCP (the tri-ortho-cresyl phosphate), for which an Indicative Occupational Exposure Limit Value (IOELV) threshold limit value is set at 100 $\mu g/m^3$ as an 8h time-weighted average (TWA), with an emergency 15min short-term exposure limit of 300 $\mu g/m^3$. This is equivalent to the North American occupational exposure limit of 0.1 mg/m^3.

Peer reviewed studies have indicated total TCP concentrations on aircraft during abnormal oil smell conditions significantly below this threshold limit. Those studies able to distinguish between the 10 different TCP isomers have confirmed that even during these abnormal conditions, no neurotoxic ortho-isomers of TCP could be detected (references below).

A Canadian study was published in 1998 by the Department of Health Care and Epidemiology of the University of British Colombia. Following complaints from crew of health effects thought to be related to oil odour on BAe 146-200 aircraft, the components of cabin air, including TCP were measured. This study was unable to detect any TCP during in-flight measurements, and was unable to detect any health effects associated with the oil odour.[7]

Another study of cabin air quality on Boeing aircraft by Harvard University in the USA, also failed to detect any TCP during in-flight measurements.[8]

British Airways commissioned a study [which was never published] by an independent specialist on indoor air quality, BRE, the former Building Research Establishment, to investigate this issue in 2001. The BRE study showed that the concentrations of all oil compounds detected in cabin air on the B757 were each less than 100 parts per billion (approx. $0.00125mg/m^3$), which is well below the toxicological threshold for humans of $0.1mg/m^3$ over 8 hours or the emergency short term limit of $0.3mg/m^3$ for 15mins.

In 2004 the UK government Aviation Health Working Group commissioned a study into cabin air quality carried out by the independent BRE. The study analysed a wide range air quality parameters during different phases of flight aboard BAe 146s and older Boeing aircraft, including tests for oil vapours. The project supplemented an earlier 2001–2003 EU-funded research project, CabinAir, which monitored air quality on 50 European airline flights. Both surveys concluded that no air pollutant exceeded recommended health limits; hardly any trace of oil vapour was detected.

In 2007, the United Kingdom Committee on Toxicity (COT) was asked by the Department for Transport (DfT) to undertake an independent scientific review of data submitted by the British Airline Pilots Association (BALPA) relating to concerns of its members about the possible health effects from oil fume contamination on commercial jet aircraft. The COT estimated that cabin air quality events occur on roughly 0.05% of flights (~1 in 2000). It concluded that whilst a causal association between cabin air contamination by oil mists and ill-health in commercial air crew could not be identified, a number of incidents with a temporal relationship between reports of oil/fume exposure and acute ill-health effects indicated that such an association was plausible. The COT recognised that further study of air quality events should therefore be undertaken to determine the types and concentrations of substances present in cabin air.[9]

Accordingly, the DfT Aviation Health Working Group (AHWG) commissioned Cranfield University to carry out cabin air monitoring for a range of potential chemical contaminants.

The initial ground investigation in a BAe146 aircraft found low levels of tri-n-butyl phosphate (TBP) and tricresyl phosphate (TCP) in air samples, together with a range of other volatile or semi-volatile organic compounds.[10] These amounts were well below well-validated occupational exposure limits.

The subsequent investigation involved in-flight monitoring of the Boeing 757 cargo aircraft and the Boeing 757, Airbus A320/1, BAe 146 and Airbus A319 passenger aircraft.[11] An in-flight fume event was observed during the study on the Boeing 757. The data from a particle monitoring device showed that during this event there was a high number concentration of a very small aerosol, although overall these represented a small mass concentration of oil. Slightly elevated levels of TBP and TCP were again measured, but all were significantly below the relevant Health & Safety Executive specified Workplace Exposure Limits.[12]

To complement the Cranfield University work, the AHWG recognised that additional information on potential contaminant residues on internal surfaces could be informative of possible fume events and commissioned the Institute of Occupational Medicine (IOM) to carry out a study. The results were published in 2012.

A total of 86 sample sets were obtained from different aircraft types, ground vehicles and offices. The residues were analysed by gas chromatography/mass spectrometry for TCP, TBP, butyl diphenyl phosphate (BDPP) and dibutyl phenyl phosphate (DBPP). The surface residues in the passenger compartments were generally lower than in the cockpit. However, the mean amounts of TBP, DBPP and BDPP detected in the flight deck were similar to those in the control vehicles. For TCP the contamination in the control vehicles and the office locations were similar, and slightly lower than found on the aircraft. Estimates of air concentrations consistent with these surface residues were in agreement with other published data.[13]

In a similar study in 2009, the University of British Columbia had reported the results of surface wipe samples taken in a Boeing 757 and BAe146 showing the presence of TCP throughout the aircraft. However, this was inconclusive and it was recognised that the results will be influenced by confounders such as the use of cleaning materials, wear and tear of the surface sampled, and proximity to air vents, etc. It was noted that TCP will be found in wipe samples taken in buildings and other public places.[14]

You will be aware that a recent TNO/KLM study failed to detect ortho-TCP in an exposure and toxicological assessment in the B737.[15]

When considering the diffusion of gases between the lung alveoli and pulmonary blood vessels, it is important to note that it is the partial pressure (related to concentration) of an individual gas which drives the exchange.

The lung tissue barrier (alveolar membrane) separating air and blood is only 0.5–1.0μ thick and the 300–400 million alveoli provide a large surface area for diffusion. In accordance with Fick's law, the transfer of gases through the alveolar membrane depends on the area and thickness of the membrane, and the partial pressures of the gases in the blood and in the alveoli.

The media on either side of the alveolar membrane are being continuously renewed; the air is changed 12–15 times per minute and the pulmonary blood flows at 3.5–5 litres per minute at rest, at sea level. This leads to efficient elimination of volatile chemicals.

Factors influencing the inhalation kinetics of a volatile compound include the environmental air concentration, duration of exposure, rate of alveolar ventilation, cardiac output, blood and tissue solubility and the degree of metabolism of the chemical. Volatile compounds are usually inhaled as a gas mixture with air and most are completely miscible in all proportions. The concentration of gases and volatile compounds in a mixture is expressed in terms of partial pressure, which is not equivalent to concentration. However, the relative concentrations of dissolved materials can be expressed in terms of partial pressures which add up to a total pressure of 100%. Solubility is inversely related to the temperature and proportional to the pressure of the chemical in the ambient gas. The partial pressures of constituent volatile compounds vary with the absolute pressure but, at a fixed pressure, the concentration of each gas or vapour varies directly with its partial pressure and indirectly with the total pressures of the gas/vapour mixture.

Thus any inhaled gas will be part of the total gas mix in the alveolus, and its absorption depends on the partial pressure exerted by that gas. Taking the RB211 engine as an example, the maximum engine oil possible in the bleed air is 0.4 kg. Of this, 3% is TCP of which around 0.1% is ToCP. In the unlikely worst case scenario of the total discharge of an engine's lubricant into the engine bleed system, 0.4 kg of oil would pass into the cabin ventilation system. This would give a peak cabin atmosphere ToCP level of 0.025 mg/m^3, reducing rapidly due to normal cabin ventilation. This peak level would thus be a quarter of the 8hr workplace limit of 0.1 mg/m^3, and less than a tenth of the 15min emergency workplace limit of 0.3 mg/m^3.

Alveolar absorption depends on Dalton's Law of partial pressures, as well as Fick's Law, and the partial pressure of bleed air contaminants would therefore be a very small proportion of the total alveolar gas pressure, reducing rapidly. Of the published levels of ToCP detected in cabin air, most are less than 0.005 mg/m^3. Another way of expressing gas concentration is as parts per billion (ppb), and for TCP 1 ppb is approximately 0.007 mg/m^3. [To assist visualisation, in terms of time 1 ppb would be analogous to expressing 1 second in 32 years (16,819,200 secs).]

It would be highly unlikely, if not impossible, for such small concentrations of contaminant to cross the alveolar membrane so as to cause organophosphate poisoning through inhalation.

Following a thorough review, the UK Government Committee on Toxicity published a position paper in 2013.[16] This committee consists of independent specialist toxicologists, occupational physicians and other clinicians with no links to the aviation or oil industries. In its summary, the report concluded:

<The Committee considers that a toxic mechanism for the illness that has been reported in temporal relation to fume incidents is unlikely. Many different chemicals have been identified in the bleed air from aircraft engines, but to cause serious acute toxicity, they would have to occur at very much higher concentrations than have been found to date (although lower concentrations of some might cause an odour or minor irritation of the eyes or airways). Furthermore, the symptoms that have been reported following fume incidents have been wide-ranging (including headache, hot flushes, nausea, vomiting, chest pain, respiratory problems, dizziness and light-headedness), whereas toxic effects of chemicals tend to be more specific. However, uncertainties remain, and a toxic mechanism for symptoms cannot confidently be ruled out.

Finally, it should be emphasised that illness can be disabling whether it occurs through toxicity or through nocebo effects, and therefore there is a continuing imperative to minimise the risk of fume incidents that give rise to symptoms.>

I agree.

2. I don't think it has ever been said that exposure to smoke or fumes in a closed environment is not a potential health hazard.

3. I stand by my factual statements. You are of course perfectly entitled to question the opinions of doctors, but it leads to difficulties when the challenges are based on misunderstandings of physiology and pathology and explanations which are physically impossible.

John Hoyte to Professor Bagshaw, 19 September 2014

Thank you once again for your time.

I am writing to inform you that I am most unhappy with the quality of your answers regarding the probability of ill health following exposure to oil fumes in the confines of jet aircraft, including the real cause of my grounding in 2006.

As with other contentious issues where there is a measure of uncertainty – you claim to have an open mind, whilst strenuously opposing this issue, which is leading to actual human harm and must now be judged in a proper, democratic way.

I stand by my claim that I was poisoned by jet aircraft from 1989–2005.

When differences exist it is normal to present the evidence to a public court for resolution; however it is clear that this particular issue has not been allowed into a UK Court of Law to date. You appear to disregard a High Court judgement in Australia, where it was finally judged in 2010 that a passenger's ill health was caused by a BAe 146 flight in 1992.

It is long overdue that both sides' evidence be heard in a public court and I challenge you to a public hearing based on the known evidence and the precautionary principle, as it is a human health issue.

The greatest regret perhaps has been your repeated failure to accept the sworn word of professional aircrew as a doctor of medicine, which continues to impact on day to day life.

As agreed in earlier responses, I plan to eventually publish the entirety of our communications (including this challenge) whilst also making available my records from the past to the Police.

Your apparent preference for the health of the aviation industry over human health is delaying the introduction of known technical solutions and medical treatments.

As a fellow professional pilot, I am ashamed to be associated with such opinions and embarrassed by such twisted logic; I will accept the judgement of my peers as to who is right and wrong where the health and safety of the public, which includes children and minors is concerned.

I regret if you feel I am libelling you, but that must be the price of formally challenging you now on the evidence and I expect a public hearing in due course to resolve our differences.

45

The attitude of doctors

As well as the courts and many research scientists, an increasing number of doctors now acknowledge the existence of aerotoxic syndrome. The process they have deployed is as follows. They check the symptoms and carry out blood and fat tests. They come to the conclusion that people exposed to toxic fumes in their working hours, who exhibit classic symptoms of poisoning and have unusually high levels of organophosphates and/or other toxins in their bloodstream, are almost certainly suffering from toxin-related illnesses. They are aware that this exposure can come from the additives to aircraft engine oil, and that a sizeable number of airline staff suffer from the symptoms, so they accept that the label 'aerotoxic syndrome' is a useful one, just as it is useful shorthand to describe farm workers with similar symptoms as suffering from sheep dip syndrome.

But very few doctors employed by airlines seem to take this approach. Here's one example. Dee Passon (see the fuller story on page 42) has had 'aerotoxic syndrome' officially diagnosed by her general practitioner. As she put it, 'British Airways [managers] hated it.' She described the following consultation with a company doctor:

> I was sent to see a BA doctor for an ill health pension assessment. He had previously told me on the phone, 'There is no evidence aerotoxic syndrome exists.' I replied: 'Don't you dare tell me that something that has ruined my life doesn't exist.' When I met him he was charming. Most of the time I was talking he was staring down at the carpet. I described to him what a living hell this illness is. I said to him, 'You're a doctor, you should be trying to put a stop to this.' He looked up for the first time, looked me straight in the eye and said 'Yes, I know.' I nearly fell off my chair. It was the first time someone from BA had admitted it. I was awarded an ill health pension. Then two months later I heard that that doctor had left [the company].[1]

Alternative or mainstream?

The conventional assumption tends to be that in the West especially, governments back medical science that is rigorously evidence-based. The treatments they recommend are based on scientific principles. In contrast, they more rarely back or fund 'alternative' medicine. This is regarded as much less scientific. It is often seen as faith-based, relying on tradition and superstition, and it suggests remedies which cannot be explained by conventional Western science, and which many believe do not work.

It is interesting that for chronic fatigue, however, the positions are completely reversed. I'll take the United Kingdom as an example here, but the attitude is much the same in many Western countries.

The official view of the British medical establishment is that chronic fatigue is psychologically induced. The Department of Health's National Institute for Health and Care Excellence (NICE) guidelines recommend that doctors prescribe a range of therapies, including relaxation techniques and cognitive behavioural therapy. The approach here has nothing to do with a scientific attempt to find a physical cause of the symptoms and to establish a proven physical treatment to alleviate them.

In contrast, independent clinics that do recognize aerotoxic syndrome – such as the Breakspear and Biolab clinics in the United Kingdom, plus many others around the world – are regarded as 'alternative' even though their methods are based on conventional science. They carry out thorough blood tests and fat biopsies, brain scans and other physical tests. Physicians such as Dr Jenny Goodman at Biolab, and Dr Peter Julu at Breakspear, find high levels of toxins in *all* the pilots, flight attendants and regular flyers who come to them with symptoms of chronic fatigue and/or other debilitating symptoms such as heightened chemical sensitivity.

You might think that once a physical basis is discovered, the idea that the illness is psychologically based would recede, but there is fierce resistance to the 'alternative' findings in spite of their solid scientific basis. Of course, the resistance is particularly strong from airlines and aircraft manufacturers.

Dr Goodman reports:

The second person I saw with aerotoxic syndrome, I wrote her a long report that became a prototype. It lists every symptom, explaining what they meant ... this lady got granted a full life-time ill-health pension [by British Airways]. Then I did a similar one, but this time she had a long, long fight with BA. Now, they just turn it down, and people don't succeed in getting their pension. They say they don't acknowledge the science, because it's 'not mainstream'.

A lot of medical clinicians don't base what they do on the science, but on what's accepted in the NICE guidelines. These are set up by the government to tell doctors what to do – you look up the NICE guidelines, which really makes a waste of time doing six years' training. In the NICE guidelines, for chronic fatigue, they recommend cognitive behavioural therapy, building up muscle strength, all of which is total nonsense. So conventional doctors can say it's not in the textbooks. They don't have to argue the science, point by point.[2]

46

Do we need more research?

At the time of writing this book, after countless air quality research studies around the world, EASA has put out yet another tender for yet more onboard air quality research. Is it necessary to carry out yet more research in order to prove that there is a problem with toxic fumes on aircraft affecting the health of their crew and passengers? I think my answer will by now be apparent to you. No, of course it is not. The evidence we already have is very clear. It is clear about the ways in which toxic fumes get into aircraft, and it is clear about the impact of those fumes on the health of those exposed to them, in both the short and the long term.

Is it necessary to carry out more research in order to change attitudes among the industry, politicians and the press? I wish the answer here too was no. Attitudes certainly need to change, because as we have seen, there is a massive disconnect between the evidence available, and the attitudes of the industry, regulators and politicians. We have to change those attitudes, but more research should not be required. They have only to look honestly and sincerely at the evidence, framing their perceptions in a different way.

That said, it is true that as we have seen, all too much of the research has been small-scale, and it has not always been targeted as well as it could have been. It also seems to be true, as I pointed out for example in Chapter 16, that some research which produced uncomfortable results has been 'buried' and never reached the public domain.

What is needed more than anything is evidence of what actually happens during a fume event. Why don't we have that? For the simple reason that *the air in aircraft is not routinely monitored.* We have seen only very occasional monitoring, such as that done in Cranfield's Muir study – which, as I pointed out, did not include a single serious fume event.

If I was to recommend a logical next step, it would be to

fill an aircraft with visible oil fumes on the ground (a fume event) from an APU, measure the concentrations of previously identified chemicals, and then publish the results, revealing to all, passengers and doctors alike, aviation's best kept secret.

In the *60 Minutes* interview on Australian television on 1 December 2013, *Toxic Flyer* (mentioned on page 185), Professor Michael Bagshaw claimed that it was not possible to monitor air quality on airlines. That is untrue. In the middle of the Second World War front-line RAF fighters were fitted with carbon monoxide detectors, while submarine manufacturers, spacecraft designers and operators of deep mines have no trouble with continuous monitoring. Aircraft could be monitored too, if there was the will – and there were the regulations – to ensure it was done.

Indeed, at present Lufthansa are using a device known as an Airsense Aerotracer to measure and 'within some seconds to detect and identify common volatile compounds used *in* and *for* the aircraft, like ... lubricating oils' to troubleshoot this problem, albeit by maintenance crews on the ground.

For example, in November 2013 Lufthansa's chief pilot wrote a staff memo specifically on the cabin air quality (CAQ) issue, which reads:

> In the ongoing discussion about further proceedings I support the claim against the manufacturers to install sensors in the air supply which might help the crew in the cockpit to make out any oil incident at an early stage. With this kind of technology implemented, we would be more able to isolate such [bad] smell sources very quickly.[1]

47

Hot off the press: a crucial report

Sunday 27 July 2014 saw the publication of a much-anticipated scientific report by Professor Mohamed Abou-Donia (Duke University Medical School), Dr Frank van de Goot (an internationally renowned forensic pathologist) and Dr Michel Mulder (consultant in aviation medicine, former KLM pilot and aerotoxic sufferer). The report details the findings of the two main tests carried out before and after the death of Richard Westgate (see pages 156–8). The paper, dryly titled

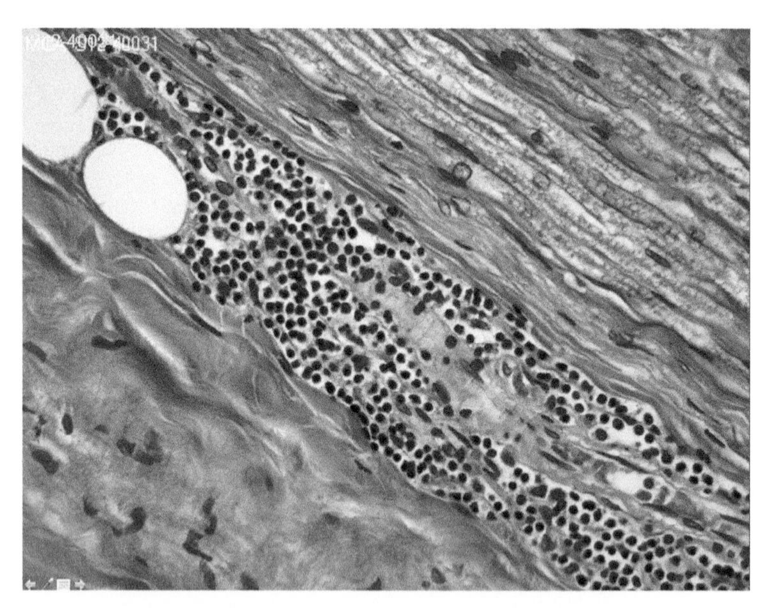

Cross-section through a peripheral nerve, showing demyelination (absence of white material) and lymphocytic invasion (black dots). White blood cells 'munching' away inside the nerve. Dr Mulder commented, 'This man didn't feel anything any more in his hands [or] feet because of it.'[1]

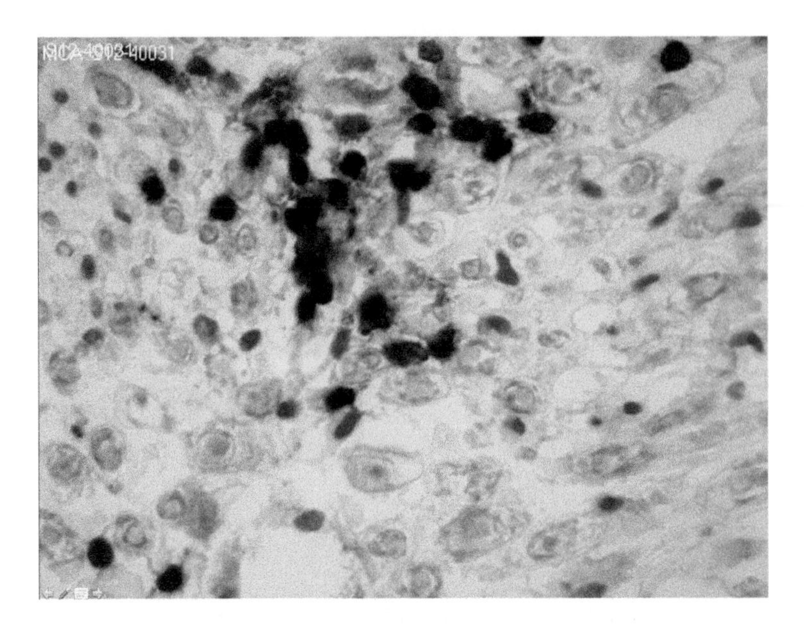

T-Lymphocyte infiltration of peripheral nerve. Lymphocytic myocarditis, visible, is the active stage of an auto-immune reaction. Dr Mulder commented, 'This picture only is already sufficient proof for explaining a possible cause of death.'[2]

'Autoantibody markers of neural degeneration are associated with post-mortem histopathological alterations of a neurologically-injured pilot',[3] represents the strongest ever link between exposure to contaminated cabin air and neurological damage.

The first test was a blood test before death which found 'grossly elevated'[4] levels of brain-specific auto-antibodies present in Richard's blood. These act as 'biomarkers' indicating brain injury. This was not a new type of test as details had been published in BALPA's conference proceedings of April 2005, and the tests Professor Abou-Donia carried out on my blood in 2006, 2009 and 2012 had similar high levels of auto-antibodies to Richard's and other aircrew.

Professor Abou-Donia commented, 'This subject was one of the worst cases of OP poisoning I have come across. In all my specialized tests for neuro-specific auto-antibodies he was the worst by far.' He added:

The air transport industry constantly overlooks three vital

> components of OP poisoning: (i) the combined effects of multiple compound exposure, (ii) repeated low-dosage exposure is just as dangerous as a single large dose (often more so), and (iii) the genetic predisposition to toxicity dictated by the individual's genes.[5]

The second test was the examination of tissues from Richard's central nervous system, peripheral nervous system, spinal cord and heart, which were only available after death. These showed clear photographic proof that neural damage had taken place. Dr van de Goot described the examination as 'One of the most extensive autopsies I had carried out at the time. I was taken aback by the request to excise individual nerves, and astonished by the results.'[6]

The report presents the results of the tests carried out post-mortem, ultimately finding the cause of Richard's illness to be organophosphate-induced delayed neurotoxicity). Unlike aerotoxic syndrome (a term the authors were careful not to use), OPIDN is an accepted medical diagnosis.[7]

Dr Mulder commented, 'Having examined this patient in life and in death, I am left in no doubt as to the cabin air connection to his illness.'[8]

We look forward to the Coroner's inquest into his death, which will need to draw on these findings in determining the cause of his death. I hope its conclusions will help prevent others from making the medical errors which blighted Richard's life.

48

Airbus on bleed air, 2014

The following exchange from the press conference at the 2014 Farnborough Air Show adds an interesting late note:

> **Captain Tristan LORAINE (Co-Chair of Global Cabin Air Quality Executive):**
> Tristan Loraine, GCAQE. John you mentioned the Boeing 787, which obviously being bleed-free addresses the contaminated air issue; of your 496 aircraft there, will any of them be bleed-free?
>
> **John LEAHY (Airbus Chief of Operations – Customers):**
> No, absolutely not, we don't think that's the right way to go at all. If you have a bleed system on the airplane – and we think it is a proven system – the only minor point had been some of the pneumatics involved occasionally gave some people some trouble in the maintenance costs (sic), we were able on the 380 to show that you can have a bleed system with electronic control of the bleed, that's exactly what we're doing on this aircraft as well ... and err, you don't have any problem with contaminated air. That's absurd.
>
> **Airbus PRESS OFFICER:**
> The air by the way is exchanged every three minutes on board our aircraft.[1]

Tristan Loraine also told me of a conversation he had at Farnborough with a filter manufacturer. He explained that the bleed air that is used to pressurize fuel tanks is filtered, and using the highest grade of filter, as it is imperative that the oil does not mix with the fuel. It is only the air that is passed through to the body of the aircraft for passengers to breathe that is not filtered.

49

How to stop the problem in future

In bringing this book to a conclusion, here are some thoughts and recommendations for a way forward. I'll start with issues related to the aircraft themselves, and the fume events that occur on them, before looking at what can be done to ensure that sufferers receive justice.

Ways of preventing oil fumes with dangerous additives from leaking into aircraft have been known for decades. Back in 1955, a few days before I was born, Henry Reddall gave a presentation on 'Elimination of engine bleed air contamination'.[1] He pointed out what was known even back then, that oil leaks were a hazard, known to cause discomfort and irritation to pilots. He was talking about military aircraft, but the same is true of civilian aircraft. Reddall identified two positive methods of elimination: '1) a catalytic filter which oxidizes the contaminants to carbon dioxide and water; 2) a separate cabin compressor that compresses free stream ram air for cabin air conditioning and pressurization.'

In 2009, after being interviewed on BBC Radio 4's *Today* programme, I received a phone call from Cyril Barcham, then a 92-year-old former chief design engineer for Rolls-Royce. He recounted how Italian military pilots had become ill in the 1970s while flying Italian Air Force fighter jets. The problem was identified and a solution introduced – charcoal filters. Sadly Mr Barcham died recently, but when I had visited him and his wife he was in no doubt that it was the same issue and that solutions are known.

Even though it was known how to prevent fumes, aircraft continued to be designed using bleed air systems which are liable to leak fumes into the aircraft.

Recommendations

Recommendation 1: No new jet aircraft should be designed using bleed air systems, which are prone to leaking toxins, for the cabin air supply.

As previously mentioned, Boeing has taken a great step forward by reverting to bleedless outside air for the cabin air supply. The new B 787 Dreamliner draws fresh outside air in through nostril-type apertures at the wing roots either side of the fuselage. It is not a coincidence that recent air sampling trials on this aircraft have revealed no TCP in the cabin air – because it cannot physically get from the jet engine into the cabin. Significantly the APU (auxiliary power unit) on the B 787 is also bleed air free.

I know of many pilots affected by aerotoxic syndrome who want to continue or return to flying – but only on the 787. I know of many who would prefer this airliner over others. The same is true of many cabin crew. The Dreamliner sold 900 before it had even taken its first flight. Total orders stand at 982 at the point of writing, with over 100 now delivered. Frequent flyers are likely to find, when they travel on a Dreamliner, that they are less prone to those irritating, seemingly inexplicable, coughs, bugs, headaches and other symptoms that they used to pick up on other flights. The carriers that favour the 787 – currently United Airlines, Etihad and All Nippon Airways – may start to enjoy this silent competitive advantage, with their finance staff noting the benefits in the quarterly reports.

Recommendation 2: All aircraft that continue to use engine bleed air systems should be fitted with filters.

Anyone learning that bleed air is not filtered is bound to ask – why not? Common sense states that any obstruction in a bleed air line causes a blockage, a loss of efficiency, which will require costly servicing. The only air to be filtered in a modern jet is the recirculated air. It is passed through a HEPA filter, but this is only 50 per cent of the air in the cabin. The other half is not filtered, and besides, the filtration which does take place is to eliminate airborne bacteria and viruses.

Recommendation 3: Airlines and industry regulatory bodies should do more to disseminate information and facilitate discussion on the nature of cabin air and the potential risks it creates.

It is a sad fact that many aircrew are completely unaware of the dangers from bleed air contamination, passengers are even less well informed, and airlines and the regulators do not help by denying any evidence exists and keeping the issue as quiet as possible.

Meanwhile all those involved, including journalists, doctors and lawyers, should take sworn testimonies from injured parties at face value and work on the basis that exposure to oil fumes in a confined space can cause ill-health in at least some people.

Recommendation 4: Priority should be given to researching and developing alternative non-toxic additives for aviation engine oil.

Do we really need to include highly toxic chemicals in engine oil? We know that alternative engine oils of less toxicity exist. Eric Piveteau of French manufacturer NYCO is someone who has taken seriously the potential for harm from organophosphates in engine oil, and is still working hard at finding a replacement less harmful to humans.[2] That would be a wonderful development, although I would sound a cautionary note: changes in oil composition would not diminish the importance of the other recommendations made here. A fume event with less toxic substances would still be unpleasant and potentially hazardous, so all of the solutions are still necessary.

Recommendation 5: All jet aircraft should carry out real-time monitoring of bleed air quality.

Last but not least, perhaps the easiest recommendation to implement would be the real-time monitoring of bleed air quality during flight.

It might be assumed that if the technology exists to monitor the quality of the cabin air in real time, it will be used. Sadly this is not the case, even though the technology does exist.

In a joint venture between German companies Lufthansa Teknik and Airsense, a tool was developed to support and ground maintenance staff in the troubleshooting of aircraft fume events in the cockpit and cabin. Together they produced the Aerotracer, a Toxic Air Detector (TAD) which allows for the detection and identification of common volatile compounds, including oil fumes, and crucially, the concentrations in which they are present.

The Chief Pilot of Lufthansa agreed in a staff memo in November 2013[3] that bleed air quality should be monitored as it is bled off the jet engine, and most people agree that this is reasonable – just as air quality is measured on the ground. Early warning of a faulty bleed air seal would allow the bleed air source to be quickly isolated by pilots.

Most would agree that real-time monitoring is by far the most straightforward solution, and it is certainly the easiest to implement.

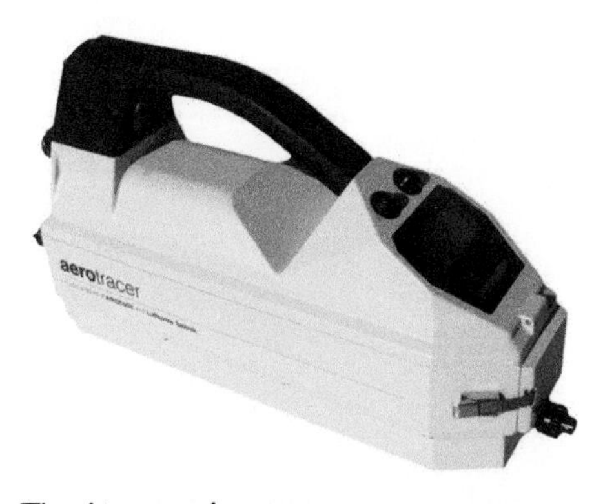

The Airsense Aerotracer
Source: www.airsense.com/en/products/aerotracer/

50

A safety demonstration with a difference

All commercial flights carry a lifejacket for every passenger. Just before every flight, cabin crew demonstrate to passengers how to use them. They do their best to make it sound important, however blasé we tend to get about it, and they are right: it can be important. Very occasionally planes do make emergency landings on water, the passengers survive the impact, and the lifejackets are used.

Very occasionally. The most celebrated recent event where passengers were rescued after a ditching was the Hudson River incident in New York in January 2009, when Captain Chesley Sullenberger displayed great judgement and performed a superbly handled emergency landing on the river after a bird strike took out both engines on a US Airways Airbus A320 Flight 1549 shortly after take-off.[1] Everyone was safely rescued from the aircraft wings or the water, while ironically photographs show that only a few lifejackets were actually worn. It's hard to think of another recent example. No wonder: a landing on water with a chance of escape only occurs once every decade or so – perhaps once in several hundred million flights.

Still, the very presence of the lifejackets shows what concern airlines have for their passengers' safety. Or does it?

When did you last witness your cabin attendants demonstrating to you what to do should oil fumes leak into the cabin, either on take-off or in mid-flight? When did you last notice that your seat was equipped with not just a lifejacket, but an activated charcoal face mask that could be used to avoid breathing in toxic fumes?

Fume events are much more common than survivable landings on water. Even on the official estimates (which, as we have seen, do not include many of the actual fume events)

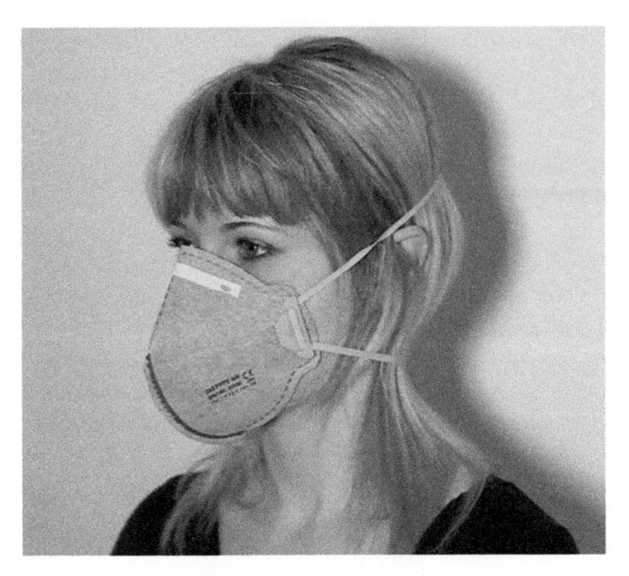

A low-cost activated charcoal face mask in use

they occur once in every 2,000 flights. If you are aircrew or a frequent flyer, you are almost guaranteed to experience at least one fume event in your lifetime. Equally every flight could theoretically become a fume event flight.

Each aircraft *is* equipped with drop-down oxygen masks for every passenger. But let me divulge an industry secret: only the pilots and other aircrew have access to pure oxygen. The passengers' supply has cabin air mixed in. So if there are toxins in the cabin air, the oxygen supply system will also be contaminated. Moreover, the supply only lasts 20 minutes. There is no escape from a fume event, and exposure could last the duration of the flight – up to 17 hours in the case of the pilot I have called Don, outlined in Chapter 2. The masks are not designed to deal with fume events, but only to assist in the event of cabin decompression, while the aircraft descends to 10,000 feet, an altitude at which the outside air is breathable. This is why the pilots are not instructed to deploy them during fume events: unlike the crew's oxygen supply (which is quite often vital, as we have seen), they would be no use at all.

Now imagine this safety instruction:

> Welcome aboard Flight Number 1234. Please listen carefully to this safety announcement. This aircraft uses bleed air taken off the jet engine to supply you with air for breathing. It is known that from time to time, toxic fumes from the engine oil leak into the cabin. Should this happen you might smell them, or see white smoke, though to be honest, it's also possible for it to happen without your noticing anything of this. Should this occur, you will hear a warning sound. Please put on the charcoal face mask that you will find underneath your seat next to your life jacket. Ensure any children and babies have masks snugly fitted first of all, as these fumes can be particularly harmful to infants. After your flight, make sure to seek medical advice, particularly if you are asthmatic or prone to other lung-related problems. We will of course forward to every passenger a detailed list of the chemicals that you would have been exposed to, in the unfortunate event of such a leak occurring, in order to assist your general practitioner in determining the right course of treatment for you. We hope you enjoy your flight. There is no charge for this additional in-flight entertainment.

This brings me to a final recommendation:

Recommendation 6: All bleed-air powered jet aircraft should have activated charcoal face masks available for all passengers to use.

51

What sufferers should do

In an ideal world, the hazardous situations that I have described in this book would never have occurred, and there would be no sufferers from aerotoxic syndrome. But we do not live in that ideal world. Many are living with the symptoms today; however much the situation improves (and it would improve a great deal if all our recommendations were implemented), there are likely to be incidences of poisoning in the future. So my last tranche of advice is concerned with what you can best do if you believe you have aerotoxic syndrome, or if in the future you are unfortunate enough to experience a fume event and suffer ill-health subsequently.

One clear requirement is to limit further exposures, which if you are aircrew is easier said than done. Remember no airline is likely to tell you if you were exposed, so you cannot assume that because the airline said nothing you were not put at risk.

It's not all in your mind.

If you believe you have been exposed to toxic fumes, and you have the symptoms I have described here as typical of aerotoxic syndrome, I have one clear piece of advice for you. Do not let your doctor diagnose you with a mental condition. Do not accept a diagnosis of stress, of depression or of chronic fatigue syndrome. I advise this not only because it will muddy the waters when you fight (and you are likely to need to fight) to obtain compensation, but also because it will diminish the pool of those fighting to have the condition recognized. I also advise it because if you are treated for any of those mental conditions, the treatment is likely to make you worse.

A false diagnosis of depression or stress is not merely unhelpful, it can be dangerous, because many doctors will then prescribe anti-depressants. To add powerful anti-depressants to an already toxic chemical stew in the body can have serious negative effects.

If you believe you have ill health triggered by breathing toxic fumes, do not accept a diagnosis of a psychological condition or take drugs for such a condition.

Dr Michel Mulder (whom we met on page 100) says:

> People already affected are suffering from a compromised detoxification system (the liver). Anti-depressants are as such metabolised at a much slower rate and will result in a relative overdose of this drug. They [the patients] are often not able any more to withstand alcohol, which also needs to be converted in the liver.[1]

Don't drink alcohol either.

Dr Mulder adds, 'Lack of energy and fatigue is caused by exposure to nerve gas components of chemical origin. It is not a psychological condition as first choice, appearing as a depression.'

Dr Jenny Goodman of the Biolab Clinic in London confirms this view. 'Anti-depressants are toxic,' she says:

> When you prescribe them to anyone with aerotoxic syndrome, the liver is already struggling to detoxify that junk, so to put anything on top is dangerous. All my chronic fatigue patients – if they say they've been put on anti-depressants, it takes two years to get better. If they say they were prescribed anti-depressants but they refused, it takes a much shorter time.[2]

Getting physical tests

There are reliable and established tests for the presence of toxins in the body. Do not believe anyone who tells you they are so unpleasant or invasive that you should not take them – for this is untrue. You need the evidence, both for your own peace of mind and to make your case in the courts. So go to a clinic – a number are listed on www.aerotoxic.org – that carries out these tests, and get tested.

Dr Goodman makes a good point: opt for a fat biopsy. The reason is solidly scientific. Some of the toxins in jet engine oil do not stay in the blood or urine for long, but they are stored for much longer in the body's fat. So particularly if you are going for testing some time after you were exposed to fumes, a test of the substances in your fat is the most reliable one to choose.

If you have any suspicion that your ill-health is related to toxic chemicals, ensure you are tested for their presence, particularly in your body fat.

Finally, as we have seen, it is proving a long and uphill battle to get aerotoxic syndrome recognized, not just by the industry but by regulators and legislators too.

If your life has been touched in any way by aerotoxic syndrome (even if you are not personally a sufferer) then please, support the work of the Aerotoxic Association to ensure safer flying for all.

And a final piece of advice:

Don't fly in ignorance. Visit www.aerotoxic.org

Epilogue

A quote from Arthur Schopenhauer (1788–1860):

> All truth passes through three stages:
> First – It is ridiculed.
> Second – It is violently opposed.
> Third – It is accepted as being self-evident.

It would appear that aerotoxic syndrome is firmly stuck in the second stage. When I first became ill in 1990 I was a young airline pilot trusting in the equipment provided and I had an innate respect for doctors and the law. By 22 May 2006 I had written a statement to the effect that I had been poisoned by the air I breathed and had lodged it with a lawyer. I didn't 'believe' that something had caused me to be seriously ill – I knew it, and I realized that I was not alone.

I have since been proud to network with many other dedicated professionals around the world who strive for known solutions.

This has been a challenging book to write for many reasons, not least that there is a beginning and middle but no real ending. The primary purpose was to help bring about change and fulfil my duty as a professional pilot. I have always been fascinated by 'accuracy' from my early days as a scientist measuring North Sea gas and in my flying career, where by definition one is always respecting limits, following standard operating procedures and striving to get the most work done in the least possible time. In addition, the results of my brain injury caused by repeated exposure to toxic oil fumes have made writing this book a far from easy task, as it has brought feelings of embarrassment and shame at how others have knowingly tried to prove that black is actually white.

In 2013 I became an executive producer of the feature film *A Dark Reflection*, produced and directed by Tristan Loraine, and intended to inform the public of what they don't know. The film is being backed by a broad coalition of interested parties (of which I am one), and includes aircrew unions from across the globe. It is heartening to be a part of a genuinely cooperative project, where people (including the cast and crew) give of their time or money in return for a share in the success of the film. We all look forward to the premiere in early 2015. For more information see: www.adarkreflection.com

I have been disappointed by many who have seen the same evidence as me over the past eight years, especially certain scientists, doctors, journalists, union leaders, politicians and lawyers – but who have found the issue too big and too inconvenient to help bring about the known solutions.

Poster for *A Dark Reflection* (2015), Tristan Loraine's investigative thriller

The film, which is based on actual real events occurring globally today, tells the story of two British journalists (GEORGINA SUTCLIFFE and RITA RAMNANI) who by chance discover aviation's biggest cover-up. A serious in-flight incident not disclosed by JASP Airlines reveals a hidden truth. Their investigation soon seeks to prove passengers have been knowingly put at risk since the 1950s. When the new airline CEO (MARK DYMOND) discovers the darker side of the airline industry and its secret campaign of denial, with information being withheld by the airline owner (NICHOLAS DAY), he is faced with a moral dilemma: corporate profit or the public's safety? The film reveals facts that every airline passenger should watch before they next fly. A FactNotFiction film

Source: Tristan Loraine.

I have always tried to simplify aerotoxicity such that anyone could understand it. For example the hypothesis could be 'Human exposure to oil fumes in a confined space causes ill health.' If a class of 10-year-old children were asked whether this hypothesis were more or less likely, based on their knowledge of the contemporary taboo of tobacco smoking, I suspect most would surmise it to be true. However, put the same hypothesis to brilliant industry-supported scientists who are denied basic raw data, and they will conclude that there is 'no evidence', but only because they don't know what is going on under their noses.

We are often told that health is paramount, and interminable research into neurological disease goes on. However, doctors are not being told the simple facts that organophosphates are present in jet engine oil, and that professional pilots, flight attendants and passengers who report ill-health from breathing cabin air may well and truly not be fabricating the symptoms.

In flying we are taught early in our training to 'agree', in contrast to the legal profession who enjoy arguing. Can you imagine two commercial pilots meeting for the first time and arguing endlessly about their flight – fuel, operational and technical factors – continuing for hours, as they travel at seven miles per minute, still arguing? Much of flying is based on simple, logical agreement.

So what can be agreed about aerotoxic syndrome?

Can we agree that a 'fume event' can occur on any airliner which uses a bleed air system of cabin pressurization?

Is it agreed that if aircrew were to get ill by exposure to oil fumes in a jet aircraft, so too would passengers?

Is it agreed that in recent years certain medical tests have become available which can prove the damage was caused by exposure to oil fumes?

Is there agreement that in September 2000 a paper was published by scientists from the United States, France and Australia which defined aerotoxic syndrome?

In 2010 an Australian High Court judged that a BAe 146 fume event flight had caused a passenger's health to be seriously affected – eighteen years previously.

The concentrations of identified chemicals in a visible

fume event are unbelievably still unpublished, yet they were demanded to be known urgently by the UK House of Lords in 2007. At the moment, visible oil fumes are officially labelled by the UK Committee on Toxicity (COT) 'low level' OP exposure and not dangerous to public health.

So how do we progress to stage three?

On a positive note, when I was first struck down by aerotoxic syndrome in 1990 I was 35 years old, but felt 60 years old, with what I thought was early onset dementia or Alzheimer's. Now I am approaching 60 but feel 35 again, the only difference being that I flew the BAe 146 nonstop from 1989 to 2005. Around two years after I stopped flying, my normal excellent health began to slowly return.

Indeed, I recall a day in May 2007 when I told my family at the breakfast table that I felt improved, with speech returned and memory clearer, but because I had by then embarked on a mission to prove aerotoxic syndrome, my marriage soon sadly failed, much against my wish. So apart from wrecking health, aerotoxic syndrome also wrecks relationships. Losing your job and having to find alternative employment while you have been poisoned but are not believed is a really tough undertaking. I do not recommend it to anyone.

As one of the approximately 40 per cent of people who have difficulty processing organophosphates, my health has more or less returned to how it was before I started flying jet airliners. I am very fortunate to come from a long-lived and healthy family, but I also refused to take anti-depressants and followed Dr Sarah Myhill's simple advice in 2006 to avoid further exposures, eat well and sleep well. However I know of many, many others who have not been nearly so fortunate, and remain in poor health, as a result of their genes, relative exposures, or a combination of both, through no fault of their own. Three per cent have paid the ultimate price and died, as their livers simply cannot process organophosphates.

Do I still fly? Yes, but in jet aircraft only with an activated charcoal face mask in my pocket, so I am ready to put it on at the first sign of contaminated cabin air, whether that be the infamous smelly sock/wet dog smell, or if there are visible oil fumes. Many of my former pilot colleagues refuse point blank to fly ever again. I fly non-pressurized light aircraft again, and have returned to flying instructing, which I enjoyed from 1977 to 1979, but my message to aspiring young pilots is: 'What you can't see can harm you.'

As Schopenhauer observed, aerotoxic syndrome will be accepted as self-evident, one day. It's only a matter of when.

John Hoyte
Former BAe 146 Training Captain
Chairman and founder, the Aerotoxic Association
October 2014

The objective of this book was to challenge you, the reader, to decide which was the greater scandal: the poisoning or the cover-up.

Many passengers are demanding to have their basic human right observed of knowing what they are exposed to when they fly. The right to openly debate inconvenient evidence is also essential to any civilized society. So terrible as the effects of organophosphate poisoning can be, the present cover-up of aerotoxic syndrome is in my own opinion, the greater scandal.

Notes and sources

A prime resource for those interested in knowing more is the Aerotoxic Association website: http://aerotoxic.org, where many of the documents mentioned below, and other reports and first-hand testimony, are available.

2 Flying makes people ill

1 See for instance US Dept of Labor Bureau of Statistics, www.bls.gov/iif/oshwc/osh/case/osch0051.pdf; OS TB 11/07/2013 Table SNR03, 'Highest rates for cases with days away from work – Inj/Ill – 2012', www.bls.gov/iif/oshwc/osh/os/ostb3571.txt
2 My thanks to Jeremy Ramsden for pointing out that organophosphate poisoning is covered in 'Prescribed Disease C3: Conditions due to Chemical Agents' (UK Government Information: Notes on the Diagnosis of Prescribed Diseases: see www.mapperleyplains.co.uk/oprus/pdc3.htm, accessed 16 October 2014).

3 Depression, fatigue – and cancer

1 International Crew Health Survey, October 2011. Available at: www.toxicfreeairlines.com (accessed 30 May 2014).
2 D. Passon, 'The international crew health survey', *Journal of Biological Physics and Chemistry*, vol. 11 (2011), pp. 201–7.
3 Results taken from the summary of the research on www.toxicfreeairlines.com/images/stories/TFA_Crew_Health_Survey_Oct_2011_PDF.pdf (accessed 24 September 2014). See also 'Illness among cabin crew heightens toxic air fears', *Daily Telegraph*, 17 July 2009, www.telegraph.co.uk/travel/travelnews/5849374/Illness-among-cabin-crew-heightens-toxic-air-fears.html (accessed 15 November 2013).
4 Interview with Dee Passon, May 2014.
5 www.businessinsider.com/the-most-unhealthy-jobs-in-america-2013-11?op=1 (accessed 22 July 2014).

4 A syndrome

1 C. Winder and J.-C. Balouet, 'Aerotoxic syndrome: adverse health effects following exposure to jet oil mist during commercial flights', in I. Eddington (ed.), *Towards a safe and Civil Society: Proceedings of the International Congress on Occupational Health, held in Brisbane, Australia, 4–6 September 2000.*
2 International Classification of Diseases Committee, Diagnosis Code 987.9, 'Toxic effect of unspecified gas, fume, or vapor', www.icd9data.com/2014/Volume1/800-999/980-989/987/987.9.htm (accessed 24 August 2014).

3 See J.-C. Balouet and C.Winder, 'Aerotoxic syndrome in aircrew as a result of exposure to airborne contaminants in aircraft'. paper presented to the American Society of Testing and Materials. Symposium on Air Quality and Comfort in Airliner Cabins. New Orleans, USA. 27–28 October 1999. Their findings match the synonyms offered by the ICD Coordination and Maintenance Committee.

5 The aircraft air

1 Judith T. L. Murawski and David S. Supplee, 'An attempt to characterize the frequency, health impact, and operational costs of oil in the cabin and flight deck supply air on U.S. commercial aircraft', *Journal of ASTM International*, Vol. 5, 2008, p. 4. Available at: http://aerotoxic.org/wp-content/uploads/2014/03/Murawski-Supplee-JAI-2008.pdf
2 Chuck Ross, 'Bring another engine for the 146', *Airways*, 2008.

6 Organophosphate poisoning: a long history

1 See http://aerotoxic.org/information/organophospate-report-john-harvey-2003/ (accessed 24 September 2014).
2 Judith T. L. Murawski and David S. Supplee, 'An attempt to characterize the frequency, health impact, and operational costs of oil in the cabin and flight deck supply air on U.S. commercial aircraft', *Journal of ASTM International*, Vol. 5, 2008, p. 2. Available at: http://aerotoxic.org/wp-content/uploads/2014/03/Murawski-Supplee-JAI-2008.pdf
3 A. Pilkington, D. Buchanan, G. A. Jamal, R. Gillham, S. Hansen, M. Kidd, J. F. Hurley and C. A. Soutar, 'An epidemiological study of the relations between exposure to organophosphate pesticides and indices of chronic peripheral neuropathy and neuropsychological abnormalities in sheep farmers and dippers', *Occupational and Environmental Medicine*, Vol. 58, 2001, pp. 702–10.
4 BBC News, Enquiry into sheep dip 'sickness', 1 September 2000, Available at: http://news.bbc.co.uk/1/hi/scotland/906592.stm

8 The tombstone imperative

1 A. Weir, *The Tombstone Imperative*, p. 185.

9 The size of the problem

1 http://newsfeed.time.com/2013/02/28/2012-was-the-safest-year-ever-to-travel-by-plane/ (accessed 29 July 2014).

11 All in the mind?

1 See page 161.
2 See page 100.

14 Incidents across the world

1 Aviation safety investigations & reports, British Aerospace Plc

BAe 146-300, VH-NJF, www.atsb.gov.au/publications/investigation_reports/1997/aair/aair199702276.aspx (accessed 4 September 2013).
2 Rural and Regional Affairs and Transport References Committee, Australian Senate, hearings 2 February 2000, http://parlinfo.aph.gov.au/parlInfo/search/display/display.w3p;db=COMMITTEES;id=-committees%2Fcommsen%2F674%2F0004;query=Id%3A%22committees%2Fcommsen%2F674%2F0000%22 (accessed 4 September 2013).
3 Plane fumes spark crew protests, BBC News, 21 October 2007, http://news.bbc.co.uk/1/hi/northern_ireland/7055102.stm (accessed 4 September 2013).
4 As note 3.
5 Details of the reported fume events are given in the court papers, available online at: http://msnbcmedia.msn.com/i/MSNBC/Sections/NEWS/z_Personal/Gold/ST%20Aerospace%20Mobile%20suit.pdf (accessed 20 August 2013).

15 Captain's discretion

1 https://www.caa.co.uk/default.aspx?catid=17&pagetype=90&pageid=700 (accessed 16 October 2014).

17 To report or not to report

1 C. Winder and S. Michaelis (2005), 'Aircraft air quality malfunction incidents: causation, regulatory, reporting and rates. Air quality in airplane cabins and similar enclosed spaces', pp. 211–28 in *The Handbook of Environmental Chemistry*, Vol. 4H, Springer-Verlag GmbH.
2 FAR Ventilation Regulation (1964), 25.831.

18 Problem? What problem?

1 Available on www.theyworkforyou.com/lords/?id=2014-03-18a.78.1

20 Evidence? What evidence?

1 Report RL 2001:41e: Incident onboard aircraft SE-DRE during flight between Stockholm and Malmö, M county, Sweden, on 12 November 1999. Case L-102/99. Available at: www.havkom.se/virtupload/reports/rl2001_41e.pdf (accessed 30 August 2013).
2 BBC *Panorama*, 'Something in the air', 21 April 2008. Available at: http://news.bbc.co.uk/1/hi/programmes/panorama/7351093.stm (accessed 28 May 2014).
3 Correspondence from Reverend Woodley to Tristan Loraine. Quoted on p. 130 of Susan Michaelis, *Health and Flight Safety Implications from Exposure to Contaminated Air in Aircraft,* PhD thesis, University of New South Wales, School of Risk and Safety Sciences, 2010. Available at: www.susanmichaelis.com/phd.html (accessed 30 May 2014).
4 Report to the Administrator of the National Research Council,

'The airliner cabin environment and the health of passengers and crew', Federal Aviation Administration, 6 February 2002. Available at: www.faa.gov/about/initiatives/cabin_safety/rec_impl/media/Final%20Report%20to%20AOA%2002%2006%202002.pdf (accessed 13 August 2013).

5 See note 4.

6 Occupational Health Research Consortium in Aviation (OHRCA) and Airliner Cabin Environment Research (ACER), *Cabin Air Quality Incidents,* project report, submitted to the FAA June 2009. OHRCA, *Flight Attendant Health Survey*, OHRCA and FAA Centre of Excellence, February 2009.

7 Michaelis, *Health and Flight Safety Implications from Exposure to Contaminated Air in Aircraft* (see note 3).

21 Real cases, real research

1 Paul Foot, 'What a shocker!' *Private Eye*, 28 January 2000. Available at: http://aerotoxic.org/news/private-eye-2000/ (accessed 30 May 2014).

2 Sarah Mackenzie Ross, 'Cognitive function following exposure to contaminated air on commercial aircraft: A case series of 27 pilots seen for clinical purposes', *Journal of Nutritional and Environmental Medicine*, June 2008. Available at: http://aerotoxic.org/information/cognitive-function-following-exposure-contaminated-air-commercial-aircraft-case-series-27-pilots-seen-clinical-purposes/ (accessed 30 May 2014).

3 BBC *Panorama*, 'Something in the air', 21 April 2008. Available at: http://news.bbc.co.uk/1/hi/programmes/panorama/7351093.stm (accessed 28 May 2014).

22 Real media attention

1 *Channel 4 News*, 'Poisoning fears', 11 March 2010. Available at: https://www.youtube.com/watch?v=FYM4soshMcU (accessed 28 May 2014).

26 How common is it?

1 S. Mackenzie Ross, A. Harper and J. Burdon, 'Ill health following exposure to contaminated aircraft air: psychosomatic disorder or neurological injury?' *Journal of Occupational Health and Safety*, 2006, p. 523.

2 FactNotFiction Films, *Welcome Aboard Toxic Airlines*. Available at: http://www.factnotfictionfilms.com/welcomeaboardtoxicairlines.html (accessed 28 May 2014).

3 Joseph Rowntree Trust, 'Organophosphate report', 20 January 2004. Available at: http://aerotoxic.org/information/organophospate-report-john-harvey-2003/ (accessed 28 May 2014).

4 http://mindhacks.com/2011/06/30/the-ginger-jake-poisonings/ (accessed 14 August 2014).

27 A cover-up

1 Australian Senate Debate, 13 August 2007. Full statement available at: http://aerotoxic.org/information/reports-and-evidence/australian-senate-debate-aviation-cabin-air-quality-kerry-obrien/ (accessed 21 October 2013).

28 The experiences of relatives

1 for more information see www.mndassociation.org

29 Balance?

1 Email from David Learmount, safety editor, *Flight International*, April 2008.

30 The deniers

1 Committee on Toxicity of Chemicals in Food, Consumer Products and the Enviromnent (COT), 2007, Tox07/10. Available at: http://cot.food.gov.uk/pdfs/tox200710.pdf (accessed 28 May 2014).
2 Memorandum by the Aviation Organophosphate Information Site (AOPIS), 2007. Available at: www.publications.parliament.uk/pa/ld200708/ldselect/ldsctech/7/7we06.htm (accessed 28 May 2014).
3 Detailed summary given in Susan Michaelis's PhD thesis (see ch. 16 note 3), pp 138–42. For Leonie Coxon's research, see *Direct and Indirect Cognitive and Psychological Consequences of Workplace Neurotoxic Exposure*, PhD thesis, Murdoch University, 2009.
4 House of Lords Science and Technology Committee, 'Air travel and health: an update', 2007–08. Available at: http://aerotoxic.org/wp-content/uploads/2014/01/HOL-Report-2007-1.pdf (accessed 28 May 2014).
5 Memorandum by the Boeing Company, 18 June 2007, Written Evidence to the House of Commons Select Committee on Science and Technology, available at: www.publications.parliament.uk/pa/ld200708/ldselect/ldsctech/7/7we07.htm (accessed 30 October 2013).
6 Minutes of the Secondary Review of the decision by the Aeromedical Section, Captain John Hoyte, CAA Reference 234437H, 6 July 2010.
7 See note 2.
8 Jim McAuslan, 'BALPA General Secretary – Summary of CAQ Conference', London, 21 April 2005. Available at: https://www.youtube.com/watch?v=sfkF27BnpKU (accessed 28 May 2014).
9 Available at: www.balpa.org/About-BALPA/Publications/Position-Statements/Cabin-Air-Quality.aspx (accessed 13 January 2010).
10 Available at: www.pacts.org.uk/wp-content/uploads/sites/10/docs/pdf-bank/PACTS%20AR%2007_081.pdf (accessed 30 May 2014).

32 Case study: Julian Soddy

1 Joseph Rowntree Trust, 'Organophosphate report', 20 January 2004, p. 16. Available at: http://aerotoxic.org/information/organophospate-report-john-harvey-2003/ (accessed 30 May 2014).

2 See note 1.
3 See note 1.

33 The Cranfield study

1 Cranfield University, *Aircraft Cabin Air Sampling Study, Report for DfT by the Institute of Environment and Health* (Cranfield Ref No YE29016V). Available at: http://aerotoxic.org/information/aircraft-cabin-air-sampling-cranfield-university/ (accessed 30 May 2014).
2 See www.colbas.org
3 See note 1.
4 COT, 2007, Tox07/10. (see ch. 25 note 1).
5 Polarity relates to the distribution of charge throughout a molecule. Roy M. Harrison, 'Aircraft Cabin Air Sampling Study, Cranfield University: Review of the Final Report', November 2010. Obtained via Freedom of Information request.
6 See note 5.
7 See note 1.
8 See note 1.
9 See note 5.
10 See note 5.
11 Royal Society for the Prevention of Accidents (RoSPA), 'Air control', *RoSPA Occupational Safety and Health Journal,* December 2008.
12 Interview with David Learmount, safety editor, *Flight International,* 2013.
13 See note 12.
14 See note 12.
15 Health and Safety Executive, *Workplace Exposure Limits*, EH40/2005, p. 50.
16 UK House of Lords (2005) House of Lords Hansard. Countess of Mar [HL 1761] October 2005, Available at: www.publications.parliament.uk/pa/ld200708/ldselect/ldsctech/7/7we11.htm
17 J. Murawaski and S. Michaelis, 'A critique of recent air sampling data collected on aircraft: how much exposure toneurotoxic fumes is acceptable', *Journal of Biological Physics and Chemistry*, vol. 11 (2011), pp. 147–51. Available at: www.itcoba.net/23MU11A.pdf (accessed 24 September 2014).
18 See note 1.
19 Letter from Frank Taylor to Lord Attlee, 16 November 2011.
20 Letter from Frank Taylor to Vice-Chancellor Professor Sir John O'Reilly, 16 November 2011.
21 Collegium Basilea and the Association of Modern Scientific Investigation, 'Inhalable toxic chemicals on board aircraft', *Journal of Biological Physics and Chemistry*, Vol. 11, No. 4, 2011.
22 G. Holt, 'A conference most revealing: aircraft cabin air quality', *Journal of Biological Physics and Chemistry,* Vol. 11, No. 4 (2011),

pp. 216–20. available at: www.itcoba.net/22HO11A.pdf (accessed 25 September 2014).

23 Public statement by media centre, Cranfield University. Formerly available at: www.cranfield.ac.uk/news/page55907.html (accessed 9 August 2013). This disappeared from the website between August and early October 2013.

24 Philip Whiteley, report of conversation with Professor Ramsden, October, 2013.

25 See note 20.

26 Email reply from Cranfield University Press Office, January 2014.

34 A safe limit?

1 S. J. Mackenzie Ross, C. McManus, V. Harrison and O. Mason, 'Neurobehavioural problems following low level exposure to organophosphate pesticides: a systematic and meta-analytic review', *Critical Reviews in Toxicology*, Vol. 43, pp. 21–44, 2013. For summary, see UCL press announcement: 'Brain and nervous system damaged by low-level exposure to pesticides', 3 December 2012. Available at: www.ucl.ac.uk/news/news-articles/1212/031212-Brain-and-nervous-system-damaged-by-organophosphate-pesticides-MacKenzie-Ross

2 Susan Michaelis, *Health and Flight Safety Implications from Exposure to Contaminated Air in Aircraft,* PhD thesis, University of New South Wales, School of Risk and Safety Sciences, 2010. Available at: www.susanmichaelis.com/phd.html (accessed 30 May 2014).

35 Scripts and framing

1 See for instance Fiona Macrae, 'If you drive a black car, watch out!' Mail Online, 22 June 2010, www.dailymail.co.uk/news/article-1288457/Black-cars-likely-involved-accidents.html

2 [Australian] Civil Aviation Safety Authority response to the Expert Panel on Aircraft Air Quality report, 'Contamination of aircraft cabin air by bleed air – a review of the evidence', September 2008. Available at: www.casa.gov.au/wcmswr/_assets/main/cabin/epaaq/epaaq-response.pdf (accessed 30 May 2014).

3 David Michaels, 'Doubt is their product', *Scientific American*, 00368733, Vol. 292, Issue 6, June 2005.

4 House of Lords Science and Technology Committee Report, session 1999–2000, p. 4.41. Available at: www.parliament.the-stationery-office.co.uk/pa/ld199900/ldselect/ldsctech/121/12101.htm (accessed 30 May 2014).

36 Holidays to Hell

1 Stewarts Law, 'Boeing 767 Flight number XLA 120 Aerotoxic Poisoning' 3 May 2010, available at: www.stewartslaw.com/boeing-767-flight-number-xla-120-aerotoxic-poisoning.aspx (accessed 30 May 2014).

2 Karen Isherwood, interviewed in 2013 for this book.
3 Available at: http://aerotoxic.org/wp-content/uploads/2014/01/TheresaVilliers_Mar08_PressRelease.pdf

37 What happens in court?

1 Press cutting available via pilots' site: www.pprune.org/archive/index.php/t-62348.html (accessed 8 January 2014).
2 Judy Cullinane interviewed in FactNotFiction Films, *Welcome Aboard Toxic Airlines*, 2007.
3 Steve Miletitch, 'Alaska settles suit over cabin air', *Seattle Times*, 25 January 2001. Available at: http://community.seattletimes.nwsource.com/archive/?date=20010125&slug=alaska25 (accessed 30 May 2014).
4 East West Airlines Limited v Turner [2010] NSWCA 53 (1 April 2010). Available at: http://aerotoxic.org/news/east-west-airlines-ltd-v-turner/ (accessed 30 May 2014).
5 See note 4.
6 See www.nbcnews.com/id/44777304/ns/travel-news/t/boeing-suit-settlement-stirs-jetliner-air-safety-debate/#.U0Vp8PldVck
7 David Learmount, 'The industry's danse macabre', *Flight International*, 23 September 2013. Available at: www.flightglobal.com/blogs/learmount/2013/09/the-industrys-danse-macabre/ (accessed 30 May 2014).
8 TNO KLM B737: 0.079 ng/cm^2 contrary to B757 D-ABOL CONDOR – random samples taken by Swiss and German Television WDR/SRF in 2009: 77.475 ng/cm^2. Difference factor in sensitivity close to 1 million.
9 Available at: www.aerotoxic.org/wp-content/uploads/2013/12/Attleeletter19.4.13.pdf
10 Email from Richard Westgate to John Hoyte, 16 March 2012.
11 S. Zuckerman, *Toxic Chemicals in Agriculture,* Report to the Minister of Agriculture and Fisheries of the Working Party on Precautionary Measures against Toxic Chemicals used in Agriculture, 1951. Available at: http://aerotoxic.org/information/reports-and-evidence/zuckerman-reports-toxic-chemicals-agriculture/
12 David Learmount, 'Cabin air killed BA pilot, say experts', *Flight International*, 5–11 August 2014.

38 Sample sizes and research agreements

1 Susan Michaelis, *Health and Flight Safety Implications from Exposure to Contaminated Air in Aircraft,* PhD thesis, University of New South Wales, School of Risk and Safety Sciences, 2010. Available at: www.susanmichaelis.com/phd.html (accessed 30 May 2014).
2 S. Mackenzie Ross, V. Harrison, L. Madeley, K. Davis, K. Abraham-Smith, T. Hughes and O. Mason (2011), 'Cognitive function following reported exposure to contaminated air on commercial

aircraft: methodological considerations for future researchers', *Journal of Biological Physics and Chemistry,* Vol. 11, No. 4, pp. 180–91.

3 Mohamed Abou-Donia, 'Occupational exposure of air crews to tricresyl phosphate isomers and organophosphate flame retardants after fume events', *Archives of Toxicology,* Vol. 87, Issue 4 (2013), p. 645. Available at: www.ncbi.nlm.nih.gov/pubmed/23179756 (accessed 30 May 2014).

4 M. Abou-Donia, 'Autoantibodies to nervous system-specific proteins are elevated in sera of flight crew members: biomarkers for nervous system injury.' Available at: http://aerotoxic.org/wp-content/uploads/2014/01/abstract-abou-donia.pdf (accessed 30 May 2014).

5 See note 4.

6 B. K. Schindler, T. Weiss et al., 'Occupational exposure of air crews to tricresyl phosphate isomers and organophosphate flame retardants after fume events', *Archives of Toxicology*, Vol. 87 (2013), pp. 645–8. See also B. K. Schindler, S. Koslitz, T. Weiss, H. C. Broding, T. Brüning and J. Bünger, 'Exposure of aircraft maintenance technicians to organophosphates from hydraulic fluids and turbine oils: a pilot study', *International Journal of Hygiene and Environmental Health*, 11 March 2013.

7 Judith Anderson has copied to me a draft letter to the editor of *Archives of Toxicology* in which she comments further on this study. She was particularly concerned about the conclusion that 'the reported health effects in air crews can hardly be attributed to 0-TCP exposure', which she felt was misleading and irrelevant, since there will be little, if any, of this particular chemical in the fumes. She also drew attention to other shortcomings in the research.

8 http://zembla.incontxt.nl/seizoenen/2013/afleveringen/09-05-2013/extras/toxic_cockpits_part_2 (accessed 22 July 2014).

9 www.breakspearmedical.com/files/aerotoxic_syndrome.html (accessed 22 July 2014).

10 Dr L. Coxon, *Direct and Indirect Cognitive and Psychological Consequences of Workplace Neurotoxic Exposure*, PhD thesis, Murdoch University, Clinical Psychology Department, 2009.

39 A lack of conclusive evidence?

1 Cited in http://avherald.com/h?article=457d4685/0000 (accessed 29 July 2014).

41 Jet-lagged, travel fatigued or poisoned?

1 Adapted from Wikipedia: http://en.wikipedia.org/wiki/Jet_lag (accessed 16 October 2014).

42 What the airlines know

1 Dee Passon, interviewed in 2013 for this book.

2 Cited in an email from an anonymous airline captain, 2007.

3 http://zembla.incontxt.nl/seizoenen/2013/afleveringen/09-05-2013/extras/toxic_cockpits_part_2 (accessed 23 July 2014).
4 www.nrc.nl/nieuws/2013/05/09/arkefly-acht-vliegveiligheid-in-geding-inspectie-wil-melding-gifdamp-ziekepiloten/ (no longer available).

43 Pressure on politicians

1 Revd John Woodley, interviewed in 2013 for this book.

44 A good look at a dissenter

1 Information from http://jarvisbagshaw.com/6_clients.html (accessed 25 September 2014).
2 Michael Bagshaw, 'Health effects of contaminants in aircraft cabin air', Summary Report v2.6, October 2013. Available at: http://aerotoxic.org/wp-content/uploads/2014/05/2013-air-contamination-health-effects-report-oct-13.pdf (accessed 30 May 2014).
3 See note 1.
4 Reported: on Breakspear Medical Group, Aerotoxic syndrome', www.breakspearmedical.com/files/aerotoxic_syndrome.html (accessed 30 May 2014).
5 Letter from Dr Jonathan Burdon to BALPA, 2013. Available at: http://aerotoxic.org/information/dr-jonathan-burdon-letter-balpa-2013/ (accessed 30 May 2014).
6 The United Kingdom Parliament – Select Committee on Science and Technology – Fifth Report (04-10-2006): 4.39.
7 C. van Netten 'Air quality and health effects associated with the operation of the BAe146-200 aircraft', *Applied Occupational and Environmental Hygiene*, Vol. 13 (1998), pp. 733–9.
8 J. D. Spengler, H. Burge, T. Dumyahn, M. Muilenberg and D. Forester (1997) *Environmental Survey on Aircraft and Ground-based Commercial Transportation Vehicles,* Harvard School of Public Health, Harvard University, Cambridge, Mass. T. S. Dumyahn, J. D. Spengler, H. A. Burge and M. Muilenburg (2000) *Comparison of the Environments of Transportation Vehicles: Results of Two Surveys, Air Quality and Comfort in Airliner Cabins*, ASTM STP 1393, ed. N. L. Nagda, American Society for Testing and Materials, West Conshohocken, Pa. 20004.
9 Committee on Toxicity of Chemicals in Food Consumer Products and the Environment: Statement on the Review of the Cabin Air Environment, Ill-health in Aircraft Crews and the Possible Relationship to Smoke/Gume Events in Aircraft. http://cot.food.gov.uk/cotstatements/cotstatementsyrs/cotstatements2007/cotstatementbalpa0706
10 H. Muir (2008) Cabin air sampling study functionality test. Cranfield: Cranfield University. https://dspace.lib.cranfield.ac.uk/handle/1826/2389
11 Cranfield University Institute of Environment and Health, *Aircraft*

Cabin Air Sampling Report (Part 1 of the Final Report) (2011). https://dspace.lib.cranfield.ac.uk/handle/1826/5305

12 Cranfield University Institute of Environment and Health, *Aircraft Cabin Air Sampling Report (Part 2 of the Final Report)* (2011). https://dspace.lib.cranfield.ac.uk/handle/1826/5306

13 J. Lamb, C. McGonagle, H. Cowie and J. W. Cherrie (2012) *Cabin Air – surface residue study.* IOM Research Report TM/11/06, March.

14 C. van Netten (2009) *Final Report on Aircraft Wipe Sample Analysis for Tricresyl Phosphate Isomers.* University of British Columbia, Vancouver BC. www.spph.ubc.ca

15 Hans de Ree et al. (2014 – in press) 'Health risk exposure to TCP in aircraft', *Neuro-Toxicology.*

16 http://cot.food.gov.uk/cotstatements/cotstatementsyrs/cotstatements2013/cotpospacabair

45 The attitude of doctors

1 Dee Passon, interviewed in 2013 for this book.

2 Dr Jenny Goodman, interviewed in 2013 for this book.

46 Do we need more research?

1 Internal memo from Lufthansa's Chief Pilot, Werner Knorr, December 2013. Available at: http://aerotoxic.org/information/lufthansa-chief-pilot-internal-memo-cabin-air-quality/ (accessed 30 May 2014).

47 Hot off the press

1 Email commenting on the significance of the images, August 2014.

2 As note 1.

3 M. B. Abou-Donia et al., 'Autoantibody markers of neural degeneration are associated with post-mortem histopathological alterations of a neurologically-injured pilot', *Journal of Biological Physics and Chemistry*, published online 27 July 2014.

4 As note 3.

5 M. B. Abou-Donia, F. van de Goot and M. Mulder, press release, July 2014, available at: http://aerotoxic.org/information/reports-and-evidence/press-release-autoantibody-markers-neural-degeneration-associated-post-mortem-histopathological-alterations-neurologically-injured-pilot/

6 As note 5.

7 As note 1.

8 As note 5.

48 Airbus on bleed air, 2014

1 Available at: http://aerotoxic.org/news/airbus-press-conference-tristan-loraine-asks-contaminated-air/

49 How to stop the problem in future

1 Henry A. Reddall, 'Elimination of engine bleed air contamination',

North America Aviation Inc., 15 October 1955. Available at: http://aerotoxic.org/information/eliminaton-engline-bleed-air-contamination-henry-reddall-north-america-aviation-inc-1955/ (accessed 30 May 2014).

2 Available at: http://aerotoxic.org/information/jet-oil-manufacturer-nyco-letter-to-easa/ (accessed 30 May 2014).

3 http://aerotoxic.org/information/lufthansa-chief-pilot-internal-memo--air-quality/

50 A safety demonstraton with a difference

1 See e.g. Heather Alexander, 'Tale of miraculous airline escape', BBC News, 16 January 2009. Available at: http://news.bbc.co.uk/1/hi/world/americas/7832469.stm (accessed 30 May 2014).

51 What sufferers should do

1 Dr Michel Mulder, interviewed in 2013 for this book.

2 Dr Jenny Goodman, interviewed in 2013 for this book.

Index

A DARK REFLECTION

A FACT NOT FICTION FILMS PRODUCTION – A FILM BY TRISTAN LORAINE

BASED ON REAL EVENTS.

FACT NOT FICTION FILMS LTD. [illegible] A DARK REFLECTION LTD [illegible] A TRISTAN LORAINE [illegible] A DARK REFLECTION
GEORGINA SUTCLIFFE RITA RAMNANI MARINA SIRTIS MARK DYMOND NICHOLAS DAY PAUL ANTONY-BARBER STEPHEN TOMPKINSON [illegible] CARL PROCTOR & SHANNON MACNAMARA [illegible] MORITZ SCHMETAT [illegible] KHALED [illegible] CHLOË POTTER
[illegible] NICHOLAS ERIKSSON [illegible] JOHN HOYTE ADRIAN G. YIP JOHN GARSON IAN RYDER SMITH CHRIS WITKOWSKI [illegible] VIV YOUNG AND TRISTAN LORAINE [illegible] TRISTAN LORAINE

HD

FACT NOT FICTION FILMS

ARTIST VIEW ENTERTAINMENT

A FACT NOT FICTION FILMS PRODUCTION – A FILM BY TRISTAN LORAINE

A DARK REFLECTION

BASED ON REAL EVENTS.

World renowned, investigative journalist Helen Eastman (**Georgina Sutcliffe**, "The Song of Lunch") returns to the UK after a disastrous assignment in the Middle East and takes a new job at a local paper to be closer to her air traffic controller boyfriend, Joe Forbes (**TJ Herbert**, "31 North 62 East"). Rather than be happy that she has finally given up her high profile career to be closer to him, he is despondent having been suspended from work following a serious JASP Air in-flight safety incident on his shift. The incident has not been released to the public, triggering Helen's instinctive journalistic curiosity to ask. Why not?

Helen convinces her new editor Nick Robertson (**Paul Antony-Barber**, "V for Vendetta") that there must be more to the incident known as Flight 313 than JASP Airlines and the aviation regulators are admitting to. Trainee journalist Natasha Stevens (**Rita Ramnani**, "The Hunt for Gollum") joins Helen to investigate matters further. As they probe the aviation industry for answers, a well-orchestrated pattern of denial emerges and they soon discover they are not the first to ask difficult questions. When JASP Air Captain, David Morris (**Stephen Tompkinson**, "Wild at Heart") dies, his flight attendant wife Isabelle Morris (**Leah Bracknell**, "Emmerdale") discovers David has been investigating the same flight safety issue for many years.

New JASP Air CEO Ben Tyrell (**Mark Dymond**, "Die Another Day") discovers Flight 313 is not a one off event and begins to ask his own questions. When JASP Air head engineer Alan Morgan (**Rupert Holliday-Evans**, "Dirty Rotten Scoundrels") reveals the industry has an engine design problem, he soon discovers the darker side of the airline industry and its secret campaign of denial being withheld by airline owners Charles and Maggie Jaspar (**Nicholas Day**, "The Wolfman" and **Marina Sirtis**, "Star Trek"). Now Ben is faced with the very real moral question. Corporate Profit or Public Safety?

In the meantime, Helen and Natasha discover both pilots and passengers are at risk but how can they prove it? This becomes their biggest assignment ever against a formidable adversary - the aviation industry - where cash pays for silence... So how will it all end?

ONE REPORTER UNCOVERING THE TRUTH...
A SECRET THE AIRLINES DON'T WANT US TO KNOW.

HD 7141 Valjean Avenue, Suite 200, Los Angeles, CA 91406 • Phone: (818)752-2480 Fax: (818)752-9339 • info@artistviewent.com ARTIST VIEW ENTERTAINMENT